The Old Copper Mines of Snowdonia

David Bick

Published by

Ashbourne Hall, Cokayne Ave
Ashbourne, Derbyshire DE6 1EJ England
Tel: (01335) 347349 Fax: (01335) 347303
e-mail: landmark@clara.net
web site: www.landmarkpublishing.co.uk

3rd edition: 2003
2nd edition: 1985
1st edition: 1982

ISBN 1 84306 075 2

Printed by Gutenberg Press Ltd, Malta

Design by Ashley Emery
Cover by James Allsopp

Front cover: Waterwheel at Cwm Ciprwth, *Harold Morris*
Back cover: Snowdon Mine, No. 4 Level, *Jon Knowles*
Page 1: Crank for pumping rods, Cwm Ciprwth Waterwheel, *Harold Morris*
Page 3: Britannia Mill, Snowdon Mine, *Lindsey Porter*

THE
OLD COPPER MINES
OF SNOWDONIA

David Bick

Landmark Publishing

The Author

David Bick is a retired chartered engineer and inventor, and was awarded the –
Institution of Mechanical Engineer's Bramah Medal in 1980 for contributions to

the science of hydraulics. He is a
Fellow of the Society of Antiquaries
and has written widely on transport
and industrial history and
archaeology, including the six-part
series, *The Old Metal Mines of
mid-Wales*.

For many years he served on the
Industrial Archaeology Panel set up
by the Royal Commission on the
Ancient and Historical Monuments
of Wales, and is a founder member
of the Welsh Mines Society and the

Welsh Mines Preservation Trust. He is also a vintage car enthusiast, having
owned a 1928 14/40 MG since 1960, which is still in regular use.

The Book

The valleys and mountains of Snowdonia are peppered with old copper mines,
the earliest dating as far back as the Bronze Age. They have been worked on and
off for thousands of years and their ruined buildings, mellowed scree-like waste
heaps and reed-filled watercourses are often encountered by the explorer. The
well known Miners' Path to the summit of Snowdon is a legacy of the copper
mines beneath its brow, where for generations company after company struggled
on through a Siberian climate each winter, ever hoping for better times to come.

I was drawn to the mystery that is in all mines when still a schoolboy, and to
the Snowdonia region in 1952. This volume first appeared thirty years later, and
this greatly enlarged edition recalls the story of more than forty of these
forgotten ventures, large and small, and some with their original machinery still
on site. Many can be readily visited and several are now Scheduled Monuments,
two being tourist attractions with subterranean trips for the adventurous.

Much previously unpublished material has been added, together with many
new illustrations and photographs including underground scenes which resurrect
the life of the miner in a world that is gone forever.

CONTENTS

Preface to First Edition

When in 1952, the mystery that is in all mines led me to the old copper workings of Snowdonia, an appreciation of such a subject as part of our heritage and worthy of investigation did not exist. Industrial Archaelogy was a study unrecognised, and a book of this kind would, in those days, scarcely have sold a single copy.

But during the intervening years, interest in the history of mining has grown to an astonishing degree, and provides the reason for this volume, which forms a companion to my series *The Old Metal Mines of Mid-Wales.* It claims no more than to introduce the subject, and is based on fieldwork and documentary material from a host of sources although regrettably in several instances little or nothing beyond the testimony of the site itself has come to light.

Mines are described individually, and wherever possible I have said something of the people involved, for otherwise history is apt to become a dull and lifeless chronicle. The geographical region is bounded approximately by the National Park north of a latitude through Porthmadog – not many miles square, yet easily the most productive of copper on the mainland of Wales.

Also included is a brief biography of David Christopher Davies F.G.S., lay preacher, mining engineer and geologist of Oswestry. On the shelves of Cheltenham Public Library and long since pulped, his book, *Metalliferous Minerals & Mining,* nurtured an interest that has never waned, and I have felt that a few pages devoted to his life would be appropriate in a volume relating to a district he knew so well.

In the course of preparing this account, retracing the steps of youth has been a pleasant task, and not without nostalgia. Old mines have much to give us, not least an excuse for a walk over the hills, and a feeling of communion with the 'old men' at the journey's end.

David Bick
Pound House, Newent, May 1982

Preface to Third Edition

I would like to thank my publisher for the opportunity to revise and enlarge this volume, and for the excuse to renew acquaintances with many of the sites, not least old favourites like Catherine and Jane Consols. Some however, which I term 'helicopter mines', I shall leave to younger limbs to explore. Two more have been added to the list, and two others are now museums with an underground experience, one being a major attraction and no less than Bronze Age in origin. There is mystery and an indefinable attraction in old mines, and once your interest is aroused, do not be surprised if it stays forever.

David Bick
December 2002

 # INTRODUCTION

'Whither is fled, the visionary gleam?
Where is it now, the glory and the dream?'
Wordsworth

In the past few decades, interest in the history of mining in Britain has continued to grow, and the Welsh Mines Society, along with others, caters for all who have similar tastes.[1] One great question has always been, when did the mining of metallic ores, especially copper, begin? There was no shortage of testimony to suggest it was before the use of iron was known, but it fell short of certain proof. The matter was finally resolved by the discovery of extensive ancient workings under the Great Orme, Llandudno, which were shown to date from the Bronze Age.

Mining for copper in Snowdonia did not finally cease until within living memory, and thus extended for the almost incredible span of nearly 4,000 years, though there were no doubt lengthy spells with little or no activity at all.

The evidence of various periods of activity is to be found scattered about the mountains in the form of old shafts, adits and opencasts, together with waste dumps which are often mistaken for scree. Often too, there are remnants of buildings and machinery, but as to the antiquity of the workings, in very few instances can a definite date be ascribed.

In general, mines, like philosophies, are not newly discovered, but taken up again in hopes that something worthwhile may yet remain; their origins are lost in the remote past. The earliest took the form of open-casts on lode outcrops but the temptation to follow good ore must soon have led to adit mining, which costs little more than surface work. It can even be cheaper, because no overburden needs removing. It is commonly supposed that subsequent exploitation destroys previous evidence, but in practice attention often turns elsewhere, leaving exhausted areas undisturbed. The columns of *The Mining Journal* amply testify to the accidental discovery of workings obscured for centuries complete with artefacts, although unfortunately all too rarely did the evidence survive. Blasting with gunpowder was introduced in the late 17th or early 18th century, and the lack of bore-holes is a general indication of antiquity. Much however, in the question of dating remains to be done, and co-operation between historians, archaeologists and experienced mining engineers would no doubt prove beneficial.[2]

In more recent times, smelting in Lancashire dates from 1717 or 1718 and eventually involved a number of works before Swansea gained pre-eminence due to cheap coal and good shipping facilities.

Details of these early sales are virtually a closed book, and since copper ore returns from Snowdonia are more than usually incomplete, it is not without a certain irony to recall that the very first published sales originated from this region – the mines of Snowdon and Drwsycoed. The event took place at the public ticketings, a form of auction, which commenced at Swansea on 14th May 1804.[3]

Returns of ore production did not become compulsory until the Metalliferous Mines Act of 1872, records for many years hitherto having been compiled almost as a labour of love by Robert Hunt, Keeper of Mining Records. The statistics between 1804 and 1847 are compared with other figures in an appendix, but many inconsistencies are apparent, to say nothing of unrecorded sales elsewhere. Probably it is nearer the truth to compute the total output for Snowdonia at more than double the official figures, say 160,000 tons.[4] The subject is much in need of investigation.

Although the great copper discovery in 1768 at Parys Mountain, Anglesey, provided a stimulus, a surprising number of mines were then already working. Shares in the following were the subject of an agreement of 1755, relating to the investments of one man alone: Abeidinant, Angelog, Bultyslum (Bwlch-y-plum), Cwmbach, Cwmmachne, Dinant, Droscull, Drwsycoed, Gwernor, Hafod Boeth (Hafod-y-porth), Helenslwyd, Heworth Tanthan, Talmigna (Simdde Dylluan?), Tanygarreg and Ustrad, Tymawr, also 'in all Mr. Owen's of Porcington, in the lands of Mr. Griffith Francis and in Sir Wm Owen's Land called Gelli'.[5] Due to changes of name and vagaries of spelling some cannot be identified, but it seems certain that the majority refer to copper mines in Snowdonia.

Members of the Welsh Mines Society take a look at the Bronze Age workings at The Great Orme, 1999. *Alison Wilkinson*

North of a line through Rhyd-ddu, Snowdon and Penypass, most of the land belonged to the Assheton Smiths of Vaynol, who owned 70,000 acres in North Wales besides estates elsewhere. The wealth of the aristocracy was beyond belief; Lord Hertford had a place in Wales which he had never seen, where dinner for twelve was prepared each day in case he should arrive.

The great landowners usually exploited their mineral resources by leasing on a royalty basis. In earlier times and in some parts of the country even to the present day, individuals or small groups risked their own money. Such enterprises, akin to gambling, have always attracted those ready to back their fancy, however long the odds might be. In this context, Hunt recorded how the miner 'is for ever hoping that mineral wealth is a little in advance of his labour. Therefore, although in relation to the ordinary affairs of life he is trustworthy, he is curiously carried away when describing the state of a mine, and he expresses his hopes rather than records his knowledge . . . Many an unfortunate adventurer has to date his ruin from the day when he gave credence to the hyperbole indulged in'.[6]

The 19th century boom in public companies might have heralded important developments by providing adequate capital, but all too often promoters and share-dealers made easy money by manipulation and sharp practice, with only a small proportion of the funds expended on mining. In such a manner, aided by falling prices and exhaustion of readily available ore, did the metal mining industry of Britain reach the point where mining shares became a music-hall joke. Ironically, they are now sought by collectors. A few firms like John Taylor & Sons proved respectable, but in general this was the course pursued.

Excluding the Llandudno area, the ores were usually confined to fault-planes traversing rocks of Llandeilo and Bala age, often associated with Felstone and other igneous strata. Copper-pyrites constituted the ore almost invariably worked, of a rich brassy appearance sometimes mistaken for gold, and occurring in solid ribs or scattered throughout the lode. The latter might range from a mere thread to 20 or 30ft in width, being in effect, a fissure filled with mineral matter and aggregates of rock. In contrast to Cornwall, the phenomenon of secondary enrichment was uncommon.

The dressed or concentrated ore usually averaged less than 10% copper. Lead was also worked in the form of galena or lead sulphide containing about 80% of metal, and thus lead concentrates attracted higher prices than copper concentrates although the metal itself was never so valuable. Lodes of the two ores were sometimes separate and distinct, but problems of separation frequently arose when they occurred together. Much rock and quartz usually accompanied the valuable mineral, and was removed by crushing and dressing to produce a saleable product. At very few Snowdonia mines before the 19th century was machinery erected, the process of separation being achieved manually with hammers followed by hand-sorting, all in the open air, or else in rude shelters. Waste from these operations, added to rock from driving in dead ground, constitutes the tips commonly visible at old mine sites, and is often discoloured by iron solutions in various shades of brown and ochre.

Wheeled vehicles hardly existed in Snowdonia before turnpike roads and railways, and the mineralogist Arthur Aitkin remarked in 1797 that the roads were so obscure that following the streams was the surest guide. But the mountainous terrain at least permitted mining from adit levels, which avoided both pumping and winding machinery. Such methods explain the relative dearth of waterwheel pits, long watercourses and Cornish enginehouses familiar in other mining regions.

Not, however, that industrial archaeologists are disappointed, for in isolation there is protection. Fine examples await them of ore-dressing sites and mining machinery albeit much in decay, of a kind that inspired W. H. Auden; 'In my Eden we have a few beam engines, saddle-tank locomotives, overshot waterwheels and other beautiful pieces of obsolete machinery to play with'.[7]

There is a certain sadness in old technologies consigned to oblivion that for generations served their purpose well, and when we consider the achievements of voluntary workers in the preservation world, it is not too much to hope that a mine at surface might be restored to working order, and once more powered by that queen of prime-movers, the waterwheel.

But equally, many sites are already beyond recall, sometimes where public money has created insipid and characterless landscapes to replace 'the scars of industry'. However, in recent years a more enlightened view has prevailed, and the concept of reclamation without regard to anything noble or worthy of respect is largely outdated. Many sites are now Listed or Scheduled, with public money potentially available for restoration. But sadly the change has come too late for monuments like the Cornish enginehouse with its lofty chimney at Catherine and Jane Consols near Porthmadog, which for a century stood high on a hilltop like a sentinel guarding the vale below. To take advantage of these opportunities, the Welsh Mines Preservation Trust was founded in 1992 to apply for grants and generally to direct the goodwill of the Welsh Development Agency, Cadw and local authorities to specific projects, such as urgent repairs to the 1819 enginehouse on Parys Mountain, Anglesey. A number of other schemes have also been successfully completed, and more are under way, such as the Glyn Pits near Pontypool where preparations to restore the unique pumping and winding machinery dating from the 1840s have at last begun.[8]

But as regards the social conditions at the mines, we must never forget the rigours of life as it was. With a practically arctic climate for much of the year, a worse environment scarcely existed, and those in warmer temperatures below ground were to be envied. Many sites had barracks where miners, worn out at forty, lived as best they could while the venture lasted, and the shells of these remote and primitive hostels serve as their memorial.[9]

In spite of its antiquity, the industry never amounted to more than a backwater compared to the mining regions of Cornwall or Anglesey, and with few exceptions the ventures ran at a loss, always hoping for better times. The irony would not be lost on miners of all ages that the last resurgence of interest, if only historical, is likely to endure the longest.

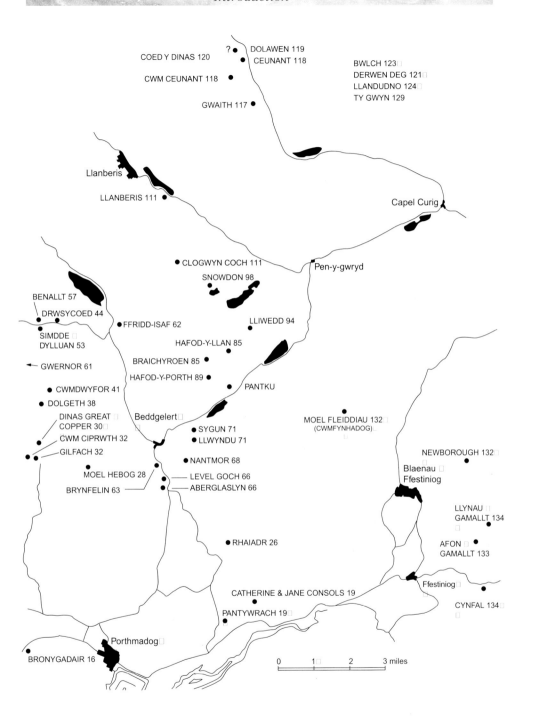

COED Y DINAS 120
? ● DOLAWEN 119
● CEUNANT 118

CWM CEUNANT 118 ●

GWAITH 117 ●

BWLCH 123
DERWEN DEG 121
LLANDUDNO 124
TY GWYN 129

Llanberis

LLANBERIS 111 ●

Capel Curig

● CLOGWYN COCH 111
SNOWDON 98

Pen-y-gwryd

BENALLT 57
DRWSYCOED 44 ●
SIMDDE
DYLLUAN 53
● FFRIDD-ISAF 62
LLIWEDD 94

HAFOD-Y-LLAN 85

← GWERNOR 61

BRAICHYROEN 85 ●
HAFOD-Y-PORTH 89 ●
PANTKU

● CWMDWYFOR 41
● DOLGETH 38
DINAS GREAT
COPPER 30
CWM CIPRWTH 32
GILFACH 32 ●
Beddgelert

● SYGUN 71
● LLWYNDU 71

MOEL FLEIDDIAU 132
(CWMFYNHADOG)

NEWBOROUGH 132
●

● NANTMOR 68
MOEL HEBOG 28
BRYNFELIN 63 ●
LEVEL GOCH 66
ABERGLASLYN 66

Blaenau
Ffestiniog

LLYNAU
GAMALLT 134

AFON ●
GAMALLT 133

● RHAIADR 26

Ffestiniog

CATHERINE & JANE CONSOLS 19
PANTYWRACH 19

CYNFAL 134

Porthmadog

BRONYGADAIR 16 ●

0   1   2   3 miles

The mines with page numbers in the text

THE EARLIEST MINES IN SNOWDONIA

Since the first edition of this book, a great deal has been learnt about the origins of mining for copper ore in Britain, and in Wales especially.[1] Hitherto, few were willing to believe that the earliest workings began before Christianity. The study was then in its infancy, and archaeologists were incredulous almost to a man at such an idea. One armchair critic insisted on documentary evidence, which is rather like saying that a house cannot be old if there are no deeds to prove it.

The first comprehensive study began before the war, when a young man named Oliver Davies pursued the evidence at home and abroad, both in the library and the field.[2] He recorded many finds such as stone hammers, bone tools and charcoal which was often a remnant of ancient fire-setting for breaking down rocky strata. Davies attributed many old workings, both for lead and copper, to the 'Celtic' or Roman eras and his study became a classic. He could not have foreseen that Carbon 14 analysis of specimens from the Great Orme at Llandudno, would prove him short by over a thousand years. The discovery proved a revelation in archaeo-metallurgy and prompted a huge impetus to further exploration, not least by Simon Timberlake and the Early Mines Research Group. Up to the present this has resulted in no less than eight Bronze Age mines credited to the Principality alone, and working as early as 2,000 years BC. The largest of these were at Parys Mountain on Anglesey, and at the Great Orme. The remaining six are in mid-Wales and generally much smaller in scale. Almost certainly, more remain to be revealed.[3]

At some of these sites galena, which often contains appreciable amounts of silver, is common but copper ore is scarce, both in the old workings and in the waste. But until recently it was claimed that no evidence existed of lead ore mining at so early a period, and to bolster the case for copper mining a novel idea was advanced – the dearth of ore was because it had nearly all been taken away, whilst the ample galena was clearly unwanted and cast aside as rubbish.[4] However, it could just as well be argued that the copper ore had never been more than in trifling quantities, and the plentiful galena reflected a wasteful ore-dressing or a surplus of supply over demand; but it is human nature readily to believe what you wish to be true. Little may be gathered from speculations of this kind, and a more balanced approach now accepts the considerable evidence for lead ore extraction quite early in the Bronze Age.[5] Strangely enough, and regardless of the mineral sought, mining in Wales apparently ceased for many centuries after about 600 BC, for reasons which are as yet unknown.

Stone hammers are the archaeologist's guide to Bronze Age workings and, scattered about the waste-heaps, are to be found at every such mine yet examined. Whether

Bronze Age opencuts at The Great Orme, with the visitor centre behind. Entry to the underground workings is beyond the footbridge.   *David Bick*

they are uniquely associated with the period is an interesting question. Another query is why so little sign of early workings has come to light in the mountains of Snowdonia, riddled as they are with copper veins in nearly every corner.

Copper, alloyed with tin, is an essential part of bronze, and the orthodox view has never doubted that the object of these early miners was copper ore for smelting to the metal. For here was the chance to establish the credentials of our remote ancestors in the art and mystery of this difficult process, and to place us on an equal footing with the Continent, from whence it had been supposed all our copper had come. Trace element and lead isotope comparisons between ores and surviving metal artefacts have supplied good evidence, but as for certain proof in the form of furnaces or copper waste, one authority has frankly admitted to 'a complete absence of any smelting debris, slag or ceramic'.[6] By way of explanation, he has argued that the early Bronze Age metallurgists used primitive techniques, where the ores were reduced to copper in the form of prills in a slag which then had to be crushed almost to the size of sand in order to extract the metal; and thus it would be hard to identify. As to the later periods, the absence of slags is put down to the smelting sites being remote from the mines, and thus never located. It may be so, but negative evidence is never quite convincing. However, remnants of one small early Bronze Age smelting operation was recently found on the Great Orme, so that the case is now much better established.[7]

Concerning the wider question as to how the tedious business of reducing copper ores was discovered, whether in Britain or abroad, in attempting to understand the

Stone hammers lie in profusion at this mid-Wales mine and almost certainly indicate its Bronze Age origin. *David Bick*

past we must be careful not to attribute to our remote ancestors the knowledge of modern man. In total ignorance of science, they were ruled by magic, superstition and ritual, and it is only within the last few centuries that Aristotle's concept of a world comprising only four elements – earth, air, fire and water – was finally supplanted.[8] Yet somehow, those primitive people managed to solve the technical and practical problems of smelting, which even today can be difficult enough for those who try it; and we must wonder if somewhere, buried and forgotten, lies a lesson for us all.

We must now turn to another aspect of these ancient mines, and pose a question which has scarcely been pondered before. Were they worked exclusively for copper, lead or silver, or could the ores have been wanted for something else? There are a number of possible uses which I have discussed in some detail elsewhere.[9] They include minerals used as abrasives for polishing, and pigments for cosmetics, decoration or ritual. It is unquestioned that green malachite and blue azurite were worked in antiquity for paint and cosmetics, and in confirmation there is evidence that a prehistoric 'peat man' disinterred in a Cheshire bog some 20 years ago, had been daubed all over with a colour derived from copper and iron ores. The tradition that woad, a vegetable dye, supplied the blue with which the ancient Britons adorned themselves before battle, is open to considerable doubt.[10]

The ritual use of body paint was widespread in human societies from the middle Palaeolithic onwards, and in confirmation there are in Africa the remains of extensive manganese and iron ore mines dating back to the Stone Age for ritual, cosmetic and other uses. The ores were removed in hollowed wooden logs. The workings were never taken very deep to avoid injuring the earth, and were filled in after exhaustion for fear of offending the gods. Specular hematite, not unlike galena in its lustrous appearance, was especially prized, and the total amount of iron ore removed amounted to many thousand tons.[11]

We must therefore ask, how much of the ores from these Bronze Age mines in Wales were sought just for metals, and how much for other purposes? Over many centuries, the sum total required for non-metallurgical uses must have been very substantial, and could have largely or even totally absorbed the output of the Great Orme workings (see chapter 9), rich as they probably were in the carbonate ores of green and blue.

With its silvery lustre, galena could also have served a similar role, if not actually smelted for lead – a much easier operation than smelting copper ores. We are still far from understanding all the issues involved.

As to later developments, little or nothing has come to light until Pennant the historian recorded a 42lb cake of solid copper bearing a Roman inscription only a few miles from Llandudno, from whence John Percy the metallurgist supposed it had come.[12] An important consequence of these discoveries has been the recognition of old mines as part of our heritage, where previously they had been treated as little more than eyesores on the landscape. Many are now protected, but let us hope the pendulum does not swing too far, where only authorised persons are permitted to walk on old dumps for fear of disturbing or collecting the minerals – bureaucracy of this kind is by no means out of the question. Meanwhile, let us enjoy such freedoms while we may.

2 PORTHMADOG

Around the coast of Wales a number of workings for copper and lead are of great antiquity. One such example is **BRONYGADAIR** or **BRONYGADER** (Grid reference 523393) near Criccieth, a work which old miners attributed to the Romans. It formed part of the estate of Richard Watkin Price of Rhiwlas, who in June 1822 granted a take-note for three years to Rowland Jones, miner, of Penmorfa and Daniel Evans, Yeoman, of Capel Isa-yr-Garn.[1]

From 1824 to 1830 Samuel Holland and his son worked Bronygadair, and during this period offered the venture for £1,500 to the Welsh Slate & Copper Mining Company which had been formed in 1825 with Lord Palmerston as chairman. In the event, the company resolved to concentrate on slate and the deal fell through.[2]

There were further developments on 23rd November 1836, when Price issued a take-note or prospecting licence for four years to Edward Williams, a surgeon of Bala, 'to sink, dig and search for lead, copper and other ores on Bron y Gader, Twll y Cae, Garreg y Felin and Cwm Mawr'. Two able miners were to be kept employed at least 8 months in the year 'unless prevented by some unavoidable accident or the inclemency of the weather'.[3]

Another interested party was John Williams of Bron Eryic, Merioneth, perhaps a relative. Early in December 1836, he assigned to John Henry Howard of Cheltenham his share in the venture, also in mines on Crown land at Cwm Llefrith on Moel Hebog. Howard was to bear the cost of forming the Cambrian United Copper, Silver and Lead Mine Co., the prospectus for which had been issued by Benjamin Cook, a mine agent of Birmingham.

Subsequently, three more Cheltonians were associated with the adventure – William Hunter, John Lewis and Henry Charles Boisragon, a physician. John Williams, however, was still involved, for in September 1840 he leased Bronygadair from Price, and appears to have sub-let it to the Cheltenham party, who had also been working 'Efel y Miners'. This was presumably Gefail y Miners or Cwm Prysor, east of Trawsfynydd, and later tried for gold.[4]

Nothing was done at Cwm Lliefrith, but in May 1841 although Bronygadair was yielding ore, Williams consented to a reduction in dues. Accordingly, a new lease was drawn up for a term of 20 years at a royalty of 1/10th.[5]

The plant included a 48ft diameter waterwheel and a 12 h.p. steam engine. Water for the wheel came from a pond at Carregfelin half a mile to the north, via a leat and wooden launders no less than 66ft high. The timber for the acqueduct cost £700 in 1838, and completion of the watercourse was marked by a celebration dinner. Many hundreds of tons of copper-ore rewarded the adventurers, and Price received £700 annually in royalties. According to one report, the cost of pumping brought the mine to a close by 1844.[6]

The time for the Railway Mania was approaching, and in 1845, encouraged by the prospect of 'railways leading from Portmadoc to Merthyr Tydfil and Swansea, to Worcester, Birmingham, Ruabon and Chester' a much more ambitious attempt sprang up about the middle of the year to develop the mineral resources of the area. This was the Cambria Mine and Quarry Co. with a nominal capital of £100,000, and certain old hands could be detected in the background.

Provisional directors included William Hunter, now of Leamington Spa, J. Williams, J.P. of Plastanyralt, John Williams of Beverly, Yorkshire, Edward Parsalt of Cheltenham, Frances Smedley, high bailiff of Westminster, Smith Wormald of Tichte Grange, Yorkshire, and Edward Ligh, Chairman of the Associated Irish Mining Co.[7] The company explained its interests as follows

'The first sett, the Llidraid y Spyty Brown Band Iron-Ore Mine, yielding about 50 per cent metallic iron, lies in massive rocks, near the surface, and is quarried at a trifling expense. There is a railway constructed from these works to the shipping place at Portmadoc, along which the ore is now conveyed.[8]

The second sett is Portryddyn Quarry, of grey flag-stones of a very superior quality, which are manufactured into plain and ornamental chimney-pieces, tables, tombstones, window and door sills, steps, door-casings; and being capable of resisting any degree of heat, are particularly fitted for the constructions of safes, baths, for lining and flooring warehouses, coping, &c. These works are carried on by the aid of eight mills, worked by a water-wheel, and a steam engine to assist in dry weather.

The third sett are the celebrated copper mines of Bron-y-Gadair and Peny-foel, near Portmadock, which produce copper ore of the richest quality in great abundance. They are worked by the aid of a water-wheel, to which the water is conveyed by an aqueduct of half a mile in length. There is also erected a steam-engine to assist in dry weather when the water is short.

The fourth sett is a lead mine at Tanralt, close to the town of Tremadoc. These mines have only been partially worked; but the ground is rich in ore, and the veins may be seen and traced on the surface, and are considerable magnitude.'[9]

To attempt operations on so broad a front practically guaranteed failure, and in spite of its august promoters the venture seems never to have raised funds sufficient to proceed. Whether anything has been done since at Bronygadair is very doubtful. As for the quarries, now long abandoned and overgrown, their site is at Portreuddyn (577408-580408) where the old buildings by the main road are used for farm purposes. A fine dam high in the hills (579413) may have been associated with the venture.

Well over a century later, a number of features may still be observed at Bronygadair, although a casual glance reveals no sign of mining at all. On the boundary of Bronygadair land, shafts were situated on either side of a large and deep hollow, the eastern shaft being 89 yards in depth. These workings constituted the centre of operations and were near the road at Twll-y-Mwn (mine-pit), a name which we may suspect originally referred to the hollow. There is now a bungalow at Twll-y-Mwn, behind which an adit was driven about 60 yards but to no purpose. The best ore was said to occur towards the south-west.

In a field above the road is a ruined building, reputedly the office, and a hollow full of bracken probably denotes the site of the 48ft waterwheel. Looking north, we can imagine the splendid timber acqueduct which extended right over the road and valley towards a rocky promontory. The whole watercourse is shown on the Old Series one-inch Ordnance map.

According to local information, supplies were augmented from a river to the north, but I have found no confirmation either from maps, or on the ground. The aqueduct, instead of a conventional leat contouring round the hillside to the west, may have resulted from an unco-operative landowner.

Near the road is a grassy mound and spring of water that pretty certainly marks the site of the adit. On top of Foel-y-Gadair were two more shafts, of which one in 1978 was still open although covered over, adjacent to a lode exposed in the rocks. The mine reputedly closed because the ore ran under another property, and bearing in mind all the evidence, the tradition is not without a ring of truth. These few details are all that appear to survive concerning a mine which, one feels, conceals a more than usually interesting story.

Journeying eastwards, it is worth pausing near Penamser (537397) where a rock cutting at the roadside reveals a fine lode of quartz and iron-pyrites. Further east, the hilly tract between Penrhyndeudreath and Rhyd, now largely afforested, hides a profusion of trials and workings. Some of these are of great antiquity, including Pantywrach and Bwlch-y-plwm. The latter, a lead mine, will not be noticed, except

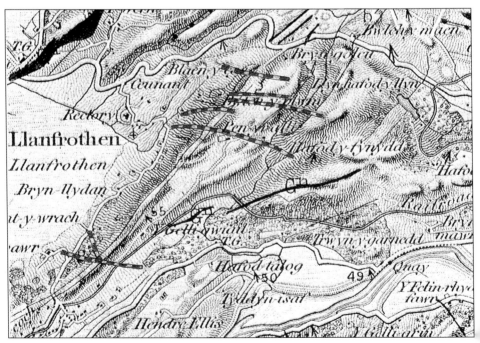

Based on the Old Series One-inch Ordnance map of 1840, this early Geological map shows the mineral lodes of Pantywrach, Penyrallt (Catherine & Jane Consols), and Bwlch-y-plwm.

to say that one part was known as Gwaith Romans or Roman Works, where a smelting hearth on a hilltop and a large lump of metallic lead were discovered about 1850.[10] The site has been recorded by Trefor Davies and J H Morris of Porthmadoc.

PANTYWRACH (617402) is on a steep hillside where two lodes converge. It was active in the 1820s, when Samuel Holland junior and two gentlemen took the opportunity of inspecting it whilst on a visit to Bronygadair, but were not impressed. The mine was apparently under the same management as the nearby Penyrallt. Some 80 years later ten men were working underground for the Pantywrach Copper Syndicate. The mine was again active during the First World War, considerable machinery being erected and 28 men employed. None of these later attempts met with success, and extensive open-workings converging on the hillside are now lost in afforestation.

According to the Geological Survey, there were two levels 300 and 500 yards long and a shaft 45 yards deep (presumably below adit).[11] An adit, which is still open, commenced below the house on a NW-SE lode and the levels extended towards the Ffestiniog Railway on the other side of Cefn Coch. There are numerous workings on the steep hillside facing the A4085 road.

About a mile to the north-east is a working generally referred to as **CATHERINE & JANE CONSOLS** (633411), a site of particular interest and therefore included here although more a mine of lead than copper. On a hilltop its Cornish enginehouse, almost the sole example in Snowdonia, was summarily demolished by the Forestry Commission in 1965, a sad loss to the industrial archaeology of North Wales. [12] The approach to environmental issues is now more sympathetic, but the time has come to abandon plans for more afforestation if the character of our National Parks is not to be destroyed. [13]

According to an account of 1856 the mine began in 1825, taking its name from the nearby farmstead of Penyrallt, and yielded many hundred tons of lead ore before ceasing work. Two of the best known Methodist preachers of the day, Richard Humphreys and Richard Jones, numbered among the adventurers in a search for lead and copper, several of whom were the sons of the lessor, Mary Jones of Cefntrefor, Llanfihangel-y-traethau.[14] 1n 1838/9, copper ore amounting to 159 tons was sold at Swansea from 'Pen-yr-alt', and late in 1855 the mine changed name to its more colourful title, after its two lady lessors.[15] R.M. Roberts and A.B. Callendar acted as agents for the new company, and lead ores worth £24,000 were said to have been raised with levels driven on the course of the lode for 60, 125 and 200 fathoms.

However, it soon became clear that very little of value remained in sight, and early in 1856 large quantities of auriferous quartz were reported, an invariable sign of desperation. This came to nothing, and the company soon announced deposits of iron ore distinct from the lead lode, 115 tons being shipped to the Blaina Ironworks in October 1856. Shipments later went to the Tredegar Iron Co. and the new agent, Capt. John Treweek, reported a tramway to the Ffestiniog railway under consideration.

In 1858 Richard Harry replaced Treweek and iron shipments ceased, supposedly due to the depressed state of the market. Meanwhile the deep adit had been cleared and extended, but with disheartening results, the lode proving only 12 inches wide,

The author's reconstruction of the rotative Cornish enginehouse at Catherine & Jane Consols in the autumn of 1860. Only the crankshaft supporting walls and a few feet of masonry of the building now stand above the rubble.

'intermixed with peach, mundic, carbonate of lime and lead ore', producing 5 cwt/ fathom or equivalent to a solid rib of galena only half an inch thick.

At the General Meeting in April 1858, the shareholders learnt that cash in hand amounted to only £103, but good ore was reported from old workings. In April 1859 the mine was said to be nearly paying cost, but the iron lode was finally given up as hopeless, a high sulphur content now being quoted as the excuse. These workings had been confined mainly to opencasts about 200 yards to the north-east and south-west of Penyrallt farmstead, now a tumbledown ruin.

Further drivage in the deep adit proved to little avail and finally ceased on approaching the boundary. Nevertheless, a little ore was found, sufficient to excuse a futile trial in depth. Plans were formulated for sinking an engine shaft known as Ross's Shaft, following the lode dipping at about 60° through old workings to deep adit.

Twelve men began the task in October 1859. About the same time one man and a boy were driving the shallow adit north-west, and a trial level commenced underground, between this and the middle adit. The November General Meeting accepted the Perran Foundry's quotation for a rotative engine for pumping and winding, and agreed to continue the shaft under the adit where a winze showed ore. The enginehouse turned out very expensive, since fifteen feet of unconsolidated ground had to be excavated before laying foundations.

The engine went to work in the summer of 1860, and F. Evans became the new agent in September. Unfortunately the lode in the 10 fathom level below deep adit proved poor both east and west, and at a special meeting held in March 1862 Mr. Timothy, a shareholder, observed that according to the reports there was ore neither in the shaft, stopes, winzes or ends, and concluded that the mine was a 'Will o' the wisp'. The company being destitute, he moved a resolution to suspend operations which the meeting carried, in spite of pleas from Peter Watson the share-dealer and mine promoter.

Catherine and Jane Consols came up for auction at 12 noon on 2nd May 1861 by T.P. Thomas at Garraway's Coffee-house, Change-alley, Cornhill, London – the graveyard of scores of mining and other ventures throughout Britain. However, it was later sold by Mr D Jones of Tremadoc.

The practically new 24-inch rotative Cornish engine went for only £350 to W.J. Dunsford a shareholder with hopes of re-opening the mine, and Griffith Williams a solicitor of Dolgellau, paid no less than £150 for an 18-inch crusher. The extent of the sale is given below, and thus came to an ignominious conclusion an attempt that on the whole deserved a better reward.

24 in. cylinder ENGINE, for pumping and drawing, complete; one boiler about 9 tons; 20 fms. of surface-rods, 6 in. square, with pulleys and stands; 1 balance-bob; 1 angle-bob; shaft tackle and two pulley-stands, with shieves to fit; 70 fms. of 5/8 chain; a skip and skip-road, 40 fms. deep, complete; 40 fms. of 6 in. shaft-rods, pulleys, &c., complete; one 30 fms. 5 in. plunger-lift, &c., complete; 18 fms. 8 in. drawing-lift, complete; 40 fms. ladder-way; 230 fms. rail iron and rood; 40 fms. bell-wire and knocker; 6 barrows, 2 tram wagons, 6 winze kibbles, 1 double winch, 16 tons of coals, 1 clock in engine house.

SHAFT DRESSING-FLOORS – One jigging, 1 kieve, 30 fms. launders, 2 large barrows.

SMITHS' SHOP – About 4 tons of iron, various sizes; 2 36 in. bellows, 1 anvil, 1 vice, 1 iron horse, a quantity of smiths and miners' tools, 1 ton of old iron, 30 fms. of $^1/_2$ in. chain, 2 large iron blocks, 1 large chest, 3 pairs plates and tops, 2 troughs, 2 benches, 1 screw stock, 3 miners' chests.

CARPENTERS' SHOP – One bench, 1 chest, 2 pit saws, about $^1/_2$ ton of rape oil, small number of carpenters' tools, 20 lbs. of leather, several lots of sawn timber, water-cask, bell and stand, and grindstone.

MATERIAL HOUSE – Eight dozen hilts, 20 coils of fuse, 15 lbs. candles, 60 lbs. powder, 16 reams of brown paper, 1 cwt. nails, small beam and scales, 4 cans. 2 pieces iron wire-work, $^1/_2$ cwt. antifriction greaze, $^1/_2$ cwt. white lead, candle chest, 1 bobbin hemp, 2 sieves.

STABLE – Two carts, rack and manger, one bench.

SAW PIT AND FRAME – Twenty-four larch poles.

OFFICE – Two tables, 6 chairs, 1 clock, 1 cupboard, 2 stoves, 1 grate, 1 miners' dial and stand, 1 bed, &c., 1 breakfast set, and sundries.

AT THE RAILWAY siding – A 24 ft. water-wheel, 3 ft. breast, with iron axle, centre pieces and ring, And 2 ft. crank, blocks, &c., complete; 2 cast-iron pulleys, 1 10 ft. wind-bore, 1 3 in. pump.

LOWER DRESSING-FLOORS – 20 fms. of tramroad, 1 jigging complete, 1 picking table, 1 flat buddle, 1 shake, 4 barrows, 7 tubs, 8 sieves, 6 shovels, 2 rakes, 6 bucking hammers, 270 lead sacks, 18 in. crusher complete; beam, scales, and weights. And sundry other articles, too numerous to mention.

The output of Catherine & Jane Consols between 1846 and 1861 is reported as 2,652 tons of lead ore and 840 tons of magnetite iron ore.[16]

Nearly three years later, it appears the mine was acquired by John Bigland, Sons &

The engine house, looking west shortly before demolition in 1965. The date of the partial collapse is uncertain.

David Bick

Jeffries of Liverpool, with a view to re-working. In October 1868 it again came up for sale, but now without mention of the engine. No doubt Bigland & Co. had burnt their fingers, added to which in 1871 they incurred the displeasure of Catherine & Jane Richards for allegedly infringing the lease conditions. The maiden ladies consented to overlook the matter and to issue a new lease of 21 years on receipt of £1000 bonus – a somewhat rapacious offer bearing in mind the mine's reputation. [17]

A Mr. Samuel Wilkes also wanted the sett, having interests in the iron deposits, and there was talk of a combined working with the neighbouring Bwlch-y-plwm, the adit of which on the same lode to the west had been driven practically from sea level. Thus was presented a great potential for draining the workings well beneath the old bottoms, and a step which at an earlier stage could have avoided the costly adventure in steam, but which was destined never to be put into practice.

According to the *Mineral Statistics,* Mereweather & Co. held the mine for several years from 1860, their agent after 1871 being George Williams. How this relates to Bigland's activities is not clear. Early in 1873, Wilkes, of 121 Bishopsgate Street, London, acquired the lease and promptly sold it for £15,300 in cash or shares to the Catherine & Jane Lead Mining Co., with offices at the same address. The directors were Lt.Col. Henry Addison, Sydney Whiting, William Paynter and Andrew Ross. [18]

George Williams of Penrhyn, agent to the Marquis of Westminster, assured the public that 60 tons of ore could be sent to market every month, there being 'never any want of ore, but a great want of proper management'. For good measure the promotion claimed 'exceptional characteristics which place it in the first rank of British Mines', and a siding from the Ffestiniog Railway and a 35ft waterwheel numbered among the assets.

Williams commenced by pointlessly continuing the deep adit, and on the 'Roman lode' work began on a new shaft which was drained by a waterwheel and pumps. It is doubtful whether a hundredweight of ore was sold, and early in 1875 the court of Chancery received a petition for winding up.

During the next two years Catherine & Jane re-appeared on the market several times and late in 1877 the Felix Lead Mining Co. attempted a revival. The shareholders all resided in London, and comprised four gentlemen, two accountants and an

The deep adit leads to the pump and rising main in Old Engine Shaft, sunk on the lode (above) and stopes covered in red and orange ochre.
Roy Fellows

Exploring the deep adit just west of Old Engine Shaft. The walls of the lode are covered in multiple shades of ochre.
Roy Fellows

inkmaker.[19] But in view of rapidly falling ore prices, even presuming any to sell, we may conclude little or nothing ensued. Thus came to an end a mine which like so many others in Snowdonia, held considerable promise in its youth, but afterwards simply went from bad to worse.

As for the workings, the only underground section which has come to notice is a rough sketch that includes the enginehouse and Field Shaft some 100 yards to the west, below which 6-inch pumps operated in a winze sunk 15 yards below deep adit, apparently via rods from surface, or else through the middle adit.[20] There are also indications that rods also extended underground and down Ross's Shaft, to pumps in the bottom level. The sketch dates from the Bigland period, by which time the engine had no doubt gone, and the 35ft wheel served to work these pumps via flat-rods in the usual manner.[21]

Before afforestation, Catherine & Jane Consols presented a classic site to the industrial archaeologist with its enginehouse, ore-floors, wheelpits, adits and various buildings, all virtually untouched since abandonment.

But the Forestry Commission, during its 'removing the scars of industry' phase, summarily destroyed much of the evidence on the open hillside, not least the splendid enginehouse, and drowned what remained under a sea of conifers, so that an overall view of the surface features is now impossible. Nonetheless, much can be gathered from the routes criss-crossing the plantation.

From the west, a public path along a forestry track leads past the lower dressing floors. They are now scarcely discernable beneath scrub and silver birch but include

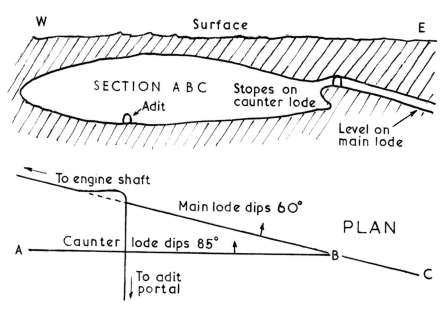

A sketch made in 1962 of the workings in the shallow adit. Note the caunter lode cut off by the main lode. The former displayed good ore, and off the plan to the right is the middle adit with a short trial level alongside.

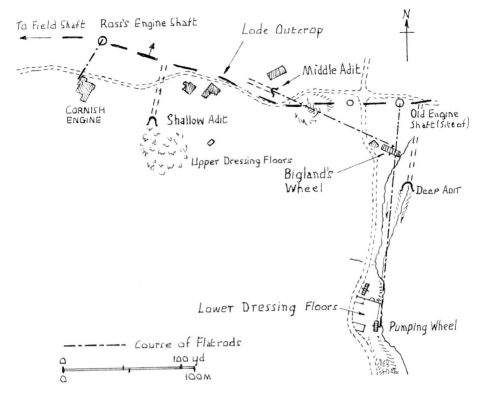

To Field Shaft   Ross's Engine Shaft   Lode Outcrop

N

CORNISH
ENGINE

Shallow Adit   Middle Adit

Upper Dressing Floors

Bigland's
Wheel

Old Engine
Shaft (Site of)

Deep Adit

Lower Dressing Floors

Pumping Wheel

Course of Flatrods

100 yd
100 M

The Industrial Archaeology of Catherine & Jane Consols. Many of the features are now partly or wholly lost in forestry or scrub.

a wheelpit close to the track and measuring 24ft x 3ft 3in. On the far side next to the stream is another, 17ft x 4ft 8in, which aligns with the old engine shaft, mentioned below. Very probably the wheel was for winding, and also pumping via flat-rods over the surface. The adit emerges near the stream between the shaft and the pumping wheel; it is now nearly choked, but gave access to extensive workings and to the pumps. The rising main and pump-rod are still 'in situ' where the shaft and adit meet. Further up the trackway is the largest wheelpit measuring 36ft x 4ft, for housing Bigland's pumping wheel; it is now partly filled and grassed over. Another trackway crosses just beyond, and more or less follows the outcrop of the lode. The old engine shaft was a little to the east of the junction and to the right of the path, whilst a yard or two west of the crossing was another stone-lined shaft. Both are now lost to view. Beyond the latter shaft are waste tips and to the right where the path gets steeper can be glimpsed the middle adit, now nearly lost in scrub. This is where Bigland's flat-rods entered the mine, extending as far as Ross's shaft and Field shaft for pumping below deep adit. They are still largely in place below ground, confirming the sketch plan previously mentioned. (Pumping the deep bottoms by waterpower in this simple manner does raise the question, how was the expense of a Cornish engine justified some 15 years before?)

Higher up, and nearly lost in undergrowth are several ruinous buildings probably including an office, smithy, stores and perhaps a dwelling. A little to the south is the shallow adit with a large area of waste outside, and as late as the 1940s it was reported that huts where copper was dressed could still be seen.[23] Farther along are the massive stunted remains of the Cornish enginehouse which pumped and wound Ross's engine shaft on the other side of the path. From here in both directions are extensive workings on the lode, ending in Field shaft lost in jungle to the west.

To the north are several more workings scattered amongst the trees, and much lower down the valley is another level, which one author has mistaken for the deep adit.[16] In fact, it drained separate workings at Cae-Fali (631405) on a lead lode running under the Ffestiniog Railway where it crosses the stream. Near here, a six-foot gap in a wall alongside the track (long since filled up) marks where the private siding left the main line. Although greatly mauled, the industrial archaeology of Catherine and Jane has much to reveal, and we must hope it can be actively preserved before the site is overwhelmed and lost altogether.

Further north, near Parc slate quarry in the valley of Afon Maesgwm are a number of trial levels (629436, 632441) displaying signs of copper and lead. In 1932, with hopes of bolstering the sales particulars of the Parc and Croesor Estates, some of these scratchings were elevated to the status of a copper mine called RHAIADR, and the details informed you that 'a dyke containing deposits of copper can be traced for upwards of half-a-mile'.[22]

With its dramatic profile, further north again is the mountain of Cnicht, otherwise the Welsh Matterhorn. Its flanks are riddled with trials for slate or metals, and some may date from the 1820s.[14] According to Harold Morris, one has been stoped and was most likely for copper (640459); it may have been associated with an item in *The Mining Journal* in August 1857, announcing an 'extraordinary discovery near the Connicht Peak' of veins of nickel and cobalt in large mundic lodes, also excellent silver-lead and visible gold. But nothing more was heard of it.

The wheelpit for Bigland's 35 ft pumping wheel, 1979. It is now much obscured by vegetation.
David Bick

The pump rods followed curves in the middle adit either by bending the rod into a large arc (above), or by a hinged radius arm and jockey wheel (below). The former was very 'Heath Robinson' but presumably served the purpose.　　*C.J. Williams*

3 CWM PENNANT

Served by a long and narrow lane that ends in a field, the valley of Cwm Pennant lies beyond the range of caravans and buses, and is almost unknown.

The Brynkir Estate encompassed much of the region, and when Captain Joseph Huddart bought it in 1809 the mines and quarries had scarcely begun. Although the Huddarts encouraged developments, the mineral resources never came up to expectations, and nearer to the present time, the mines have defeated more than one attempt to correlate written records or to marry them with evidence on the ground.

The first, **MOEL HEBOG** (558472) is high on the mountain of that name, where in August 1837 the Crown granted a lease to William Morgan Buckingham to work 'within the piece of waste land containing about 199 acres 15 perches called Ochr Cwm Llefrith'. Whether the site had seen earlier activity is uncertain; it is shown as a copper mine on the 1840 Ordnance map.

After a short while, Buckingham abandoned the mine and died soon afterwards, and a Henry Marshall took over. He spent about £300 abortively driving a level, a new lease of 164 acres being authorised for a term of 21 years from 10 October 1847. Marshall agreed to keep four men constantly at work during eight months of the year, 'the situation being so exposed that in the winter months no work can be done'. But severe problems of transport and access over the lands of adjoining owners, combined with worsening prospects, caused the lease soon to be surrendered.[1]

TO THE SHAREHOLDERS OF THE DINAS GREAT CONSOLS.

REPORT OF THE SUB-COMMITTEE.

It affords the committee very much pleasure to inform the shareholders that three trials for gold have been made by Berdan's crushing machine on the quartz from the Dinas, and the sulphur from the Moel Hebog, and that in two instances they have produced the most satisfactory results. The quartz from the Dinas (83 lbs.) yielded no gold; but 95 lbs. of mundic, or sulphur, from the Moel Hebog Mine yielded 1 dwt. 3 grs.; equal to 1 oz. 6 dwts. 12 grs. per ton. The committee resolved that no report should be made of this trial until it had been confirmed by a second, on a larger sample, which has now been made, the result showing an increase in the quantity of gold. This second trial was with the eighth of a ton, or 280 lbs., the yield being at the rate of 1 oz. 18 dwts. to the ton; worth £7 12s. at the market price. The sulphur exists in great abundance, and can be raised at a very small cost. Making a very liberal allowance for the working, it would leave a nett profit of between £6 and £7 per ton; and as one machine will crush and amalgamate 20 tons per day, it is confidently anticipated, by all who have witnessed the experiments, that the clear profits will be £2000 per month, paying large and early dividends upon the shares. Under these very encouraging circumstances, the committee can have no hesitation in recommending that a crushing and amalgamating machine should be immediately put up; and they have a strong conviction, that when fully developed, this mine will not be inferior to the best-paying mines in the kingdom.

By order of the board,

76, King William-street, Jan. 5, 1854.   JOHN BRYDIE, Chairman.

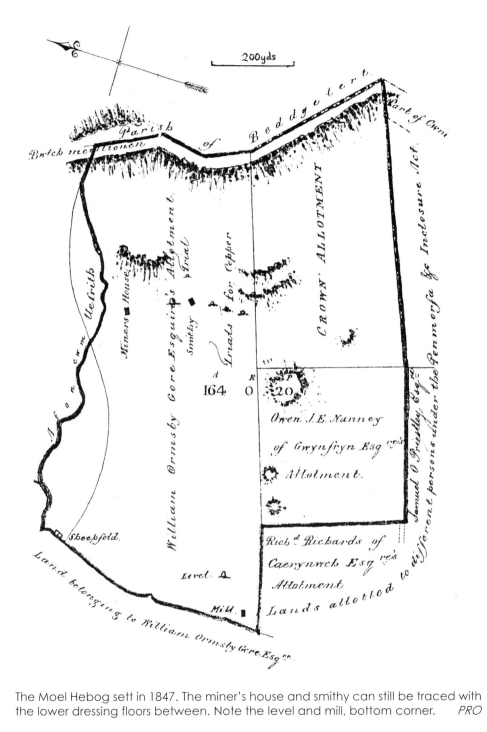

The Moel Hebog sett in 1847. The miner's house and smithy can still be traced with the lower dressing floors between. Note the level and mill, bottom corner.   *PRO*

The ruinous building outside the lofty entrance to the main level was probably an ore-dressing shed. *John Burman*

To continue the history of Moel Hebog, we must journey up the valley to Braich-y-Dinas, where a number of trial levels penetrate the steep hillside and no doubt mark the remnants of **DINAS GREAT COPPER** (531484). Early in 1853 a London company promoted the venture with gusto, the sett consisting of 500 acres bounded by Gilfach and Blaen-y-Pennant mines. At a Special Meeting William Lelean claimed that 'as in some instances the side of the land was perpendicular they had only, as it were, to open a door and take the copper out . . . It appeared to be an entire mountain of copper, and he could form no other opinion'.[2]

But notwithstanding the cautionary observations of Nicholas Ennor of Wiveliscombe, Professor W. White submitted a glowing report in June 1853 referring to six levels for copper and another driven for 2 fathoms 'on a sequestered face of the mountain exposing a very promising lode of silver-lead'. No. 1 or Brydie's level revealed, so he asserted, a lode of blue and yellow ore with streaks of copper carbonate, and from No. 4 level 'on a magnificent lode large masses of ore were disengaged by blasting'.[3]

W.T. Fox of Gilfach was appointed agent, but before the end of the year his equally optimistic comments came under fire from Capt. Matthew Francis, late chief agent to John Taylor & Sons' Lisburne Mines in Cardiganshire, in a report to the management. Francis also introduced an unexpected development by advising trials on ores both from Dinas and Moel Hebog as likely to yield gold.[4] The precious metal existed in every mining district according to John Calvert, whose recently published *Gold Rocks of Great Britain and Ireland* had caused something of a furore, but it was significant that such recommendations generally amounted to little more than a last attempt to salvage a doomed concern.

A further reason for the interest in Moel Hebog becomes apparent when the vendors of Dinas, who it appears felt indebted to the company, had offered that mine in compensation. In consequence Moel Hebog became incorporated, the new joint company being known as Dinas Great Consols.[5]

From the shareholders' standpoint prospects appeared brighter, for early in 1854 the chairman, John Brydie, announced that Berdan's crushing machine had yielded 1 oz. 6 dwt of gold per ton of iron-pyrites from Moel Hebog, based on a sample of 95 lb. A larger batch gave even better results, and it was 'confidently expected that the clear profits will be £2000 per month, paying large and early dividends.[6]

The crushing machine had been patented and set up in London by Henry Berdan, whose offer to analyse samples free of charge proved irresistible. We can only guess in how many instances favourable results occurred from 'salting' somewhere along the line, rather than from genuine auriferous material, but it may not be quite without signficance that Berdan shortly afterwards departed to foreign shores.[7]

Cavernous stopes at Moel Hebog testify to the ore removed.   *John Burman*

With its undertones of fraud, and almost total lack of real discoveries, the gold-mining mania soon collapsed, and Dinas Great Consols likewise faded into oblivion. It later transpired that Lelean was a lessee of Moel Hebog at the time of incorporation, and had twice passed through the Insolvent Debtors Court, confirming a strong suspicion of fraud from beginning to end.[8]

Subsequently, Moel Hebog seems to have lain idle for many years, becoming known as Cwm Llefrith in 1883 when three partners, H. Thomas, H. Jones and I. Davies were involved. In July 1886, Frederick William Jones of Fountain Lodge, Liscard, Cheshire, acquired a take-note from the Crown, and in the next month the Moel Hebog Copper Mining Co. Ltd. was formed. J.J. Warry acted as secretary, and Jones received £10,000 divided equally into cash and shares for his efforts. Consulting Engineers were J. Craig & Co., 34 South John Street, Liverpool.[9]

In 1888, the name changed to Glistening Valley – hardly an apt description, though certainly more evocative. Forty-four men were employed, half being below ground.[10] After a year, although the Hebog company still existed at least on paper, the Cwm Llefrith Co. Ltd. was formed with registered offices in London. F.W. Jones again controlled a majority of shares, and the secretary was D. Oliver Mason; six months later the venture descended into liquidation. [11] J. I. C. Boyd's *Narrow Gauge Railways in South Caernarvonshire* records how about 40 bags of copper ore travelled over part of the Croesor tramway early in 1889, and this probably represented some of the 7 tons officially returned in that year. In the September, two miners were injured by an explosion of blasting gelatine.

The schedule below gives a good idea of the plant and equipment. [11]

Wooden building roofed with slate 36ft x 14ft.
Powder store built of wood in a short level.
Bottom Dressing floor. Dressing Shed 22ft x 13ft stone with corrugated-iron roof. New
   jigger tub for washing ore and hand barrow.
Smithy built of stone with double blast bellows, anvil, etc. 276 ore bags.
Upper Dressing floor. Stone built Dressing shed 22ft x 15ft.
6 cobbing hammers, spalling hammer, 2 sorting boxes, three hand sieves etc.
2 small sleds for carrying copper down at the railway.

In common with a number of mines in Snowdonia, its altitude placed Moel Hebog at a grave disadvantage in respect of both transport and water-power. The workings were never tried in depth, but a good rib of copper-pyrites left behind in the roof of the main level at the lower dressing floors, is a guide to the ore taken away. The site testifies to a good deal of manual effort unrelieved by power, and since methods hardly changed over the years, to correlate the various features with different periods of working is a difficult task.

Piles of hand-cobbed waste, without any sign of finely pulverized material or slimes, bear witness to the absence of crushing machinery, and in the lower part of the sett are two short parallel walls of no apparent purpose.

Adjacent to Braich-y-Dinas are **GILFACH** (531477) and **CWM CIPRWTH** (526478) – one being on a steep hillside and the other on a plateau above. 40 tons of copper ore were sold from Gilfach in 1828/9, and its origins have been attributed by one author to this period. [12]

Details of the mines were published in a prospectus issued in the summer of 1850 by the Mining Company of Wales, a mushroom venture promoted on a grand scale in London. The secretary was St. Pierre Foley, 'of Irish mining and geological celebrity'. The company aimed to develop various mines and slate workings throughout the Principality, including Rhossyd and Wrysgan quarries, the Denbigh slab quarries, Cwmorthin lead mine and three mines in Cwm Pennant – Gilfach, Cwm Ciprwth and Blaen-y-Pennant.

The following extract from the prospectus reflects a typical share-pushing style of the period, the reference to the same lodes being worked at Drws-y-Coed having not the slightest justification. [13] But it is clear that much had been done by earlier workers.

GILVACH AND CWM CIPRWTH COPPER MINES

The extent of these mines on the lodes is about two miles. Two lodes have been proved in distant places along their bearings. On Cwm Ciprwth there is a water-wheel with pumps, &c., and a shaft with several shallow drivings therefrom. The greatest depth about 18 fathoms, at the bottom of which there is a lode of 8 feet wide, well mixed with copper ore, and carrying a continuous rib of 2 feet, nearly full of solid ore. This lode is very promising – as gossany and kindly as any miner could wish, and likely to improve still further in depth. More powerful machinery must, however, be erected, and a change made in the water-course, to put this mine to work, to make those high returns promised by present indications.

Gilvach is undoubtedly a great mine. It has already produced several hundred tons of ore at shallow workings, and now shows on small drivings at bottom of winze, or subshafts, a lode of 4 feet wide, quite solid. Some small shipments of ore have been lately made, from trials at these bottoms, and heaps of ore from the same are now on the washing floors. The adit leading to the winze shafts is, however, rather tortuous, as indeed, are the winzes themselves, and the water is strong at bottom; therefore, it is advisable to open a new adit level, to command the bottoms (see report), which, when done, will render available at once some thousand fathoms of rich ore ground, and some hundred fathoms of a most productive lode.

But, besides all this, there is being worked a deep adit level, some 12 or 13 fathoms still lower down the mountain, that has just cut one of the southern lodes, parallel and within a few fathoms of the former, which shows rich copper ore, and is very promising.

It need only to be remarked, in confirmation of the favourable opinion reported of these mines, that the same lodes have been worked on for several years, and are now being worked, on the north eastern side of the mountain, in the celebrated mines of Drwsy Coed, &c., distant, in horizontal range, from Gilvach 990 fathoms, and at present producing immense quantities of ore, reported 1000 tons monthly. Indeed, several railway waggons are seen constantly in active service, bearing their rich burdens to the well-arranged premises of the company at Carnarvon for shipping.

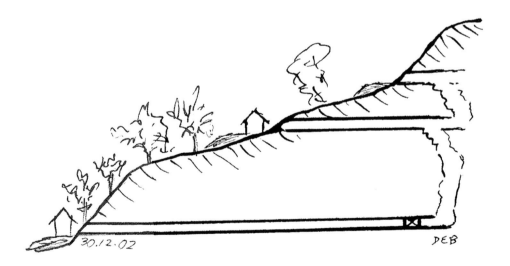

A section of Gilfach made in 1952, not to scale. The deep adit is 375 paces long. Near the end are a rise and a crosscut driven south-west 130 paces through several poor copper lodes.

Outside the middle adit at Gilfach. In front of the retaining wall is a long low stone bench for cobbing the ore with hammers. *David Bick*

The restored pumping and winding waterwheel less buckets and launders at Cwm Ciprwth, showing the flat-rod leading to the shaft. *Harold Morris*

Another view, along the line of flat-rods to the shaft.   *Harold Morris*

Soon afterwards, four men were said to be driving on a north-west lode from No.1 shaft at Cwm Ciprwth, worth 3 tons of ore per fathom, but less than two years after launching the company a worried investor wrote to *The Mining Journal* 'Can any of your correspondents inform a holder of 24 shares what has become of the concoctors of this scheme'. The appeal evoked a feeble response from Foley, who admitted that the business had now dissolved. However, there must have been a revival in some form or another, for Gilfach returned 25 tons of copper ore in 1854.

The next evidence of mining is at Cwm Ciprwth, which was taken up by the Brynkir Gold Exploration Syndicate, formed in 1889. The Directors included C.H.C. Huddart, and all had London addresses. [14] In 1890, 12 men were working below ground and six above, the agent being John Sandoe.[15a] The number of miners halved in 1891/2, and by 1894 the company had declined into liquidation.

From a detailed inventory dated October 1900,[15b] we learn that there were three storerooms, an upper and lower smithy and an office. The latter included a 2ft rule, a spirit level, weighing machine, five account books, and such homely items as a table and four chairs, an iron bed with blankets, sheets and a quilt, two pillows, a washstand, jug and basin, a looking-glass, and an inkstand. Also listed were 2,730ft of 'railroad' and at Gilfach a crushing mill with a raff-wheel (a kind of lift) for feeding ore to a jigger. Cwm Ciprwth boasted a large iron waterwheel, an 'enginehouse', a winding drum and cable, one large iron pulley, a crab-winch, three pump-rods and much else. The assets underground included six ladders, a turntree or hand-windlass, cables and a large quantity of timber.

The winding drum, geared up from the waterwheel axle. In the centre of the picture are the radial arms for working the friction-clutch; the iron hand-lever has been broken off close to the collar. *Harold Morris*

This detail shows the restored angle-bob at the shaft, complete with iron pedestal-bearings. *Harold Morris*

The crab-winch is standing next to the open shaft at Gilfach, before restoration of the site. *C.J.Williams*

A century later, the remains at Gilfach are mantled in woodland on a steep hillside, at the bottom of which is the deep adit, a ruinous building and a substantial masonry wheelpit integral with the walls of the crusher-house. The lack of waste suggests that very little ore was processed. Outside the middle adit are the ruins of another building and a retaining wall with a long stone bench which probably denotes where the ore was hand-cobbed or broken down with hammers to remove the waste rock and gangue. At the end of this adit, steps with a hand-rail descend into dangerous stopes. More to the west, the top adit goes straight into a rockface and the floor is stoped out just inside. Below it, a leat lined in places with flags runs past another ruin as far as the waste-dumps from the middle adit, where it descends steeply for driving the crushing mill in the valley below.

Much more survives at Cwm Ciprwth, where, due to its isolation, the machinery was not worth the scrap merchant's trouble. I well recall my first visit 50 years ago, when standing against the sky, the winding drum and rusting iron waterwheel were a wonderful sight, and resurrected the scene as it had been over half a century before. Some of the timbers bore the stamp BGES, which suggested a date of 1889/90, but the plant may have come secondhand from elsewhere – the wheel carried the name 'Dingey & Son, Truro'.[16,17a] Fortunately, this unique survivor has been restored by the Welsh Development Agency and the Snowdonia National Park under the management of Peter Crew, and thus it pleasing to record that the dream of reconstruction expressed in the first edition of this volume has to a large extent come true. Cwm Ciprwth well rewards the effort to get there, and is a first-class practical introduction to the machinery typical of the nineteenth century metal mines, devoid of noise or pollution, but now almost unknown in its original and proper setting.

There is public access to both mines from the new bridge over Afon Dwyfor at grid reference 532477, although no footpaths as such exist. Their total output is unrecorded, but Gilfach was clearly the more productive though like many others, it failed badly in the final endeavours.

In *The Old Metal Mines of mid-Wales*, Part 5, I recorded an unusual metal and slate operation at Cyfannedd near Arthog, and recently another has come to light near the end of the road up the Pennant valley. The site is known as Dol-Ifan-Githin, Dolgarth or DOLGETH (537495), where a group of buildings shown on sales particulars of 1896 survive as mostly ruins and serve for farming purposes.[17b] As regards the mining history, these particulars together with the physical testimony provide what little we know. The picture which emerges is intriguing, but far from clear.

The sale encompassed both a slate quarry and 'copper mine', although the only excuse for including the latter was a shaft and adit marked on the accompanying plan. However, the inventory gives tantalising hints of something more. There was a waterwheel and crushing rolls and the 'machine house' (slate-dressing mill) included

A view of Dolgeth from the quarry incline with the slate dressing-shed grafted onto the waterwheel pit and crusher-house on the right. Behind is the smithy and office, as shown on the sale plan of 1896. *David Bick*

DOLGETH SLATE QUARRY & COPPER MINE.

County of Carnarvon.

PARISH OF DOLBENMAEN,

FORMERLY THE

PARISH OF LLANFIHANGEL-Y-PENNANT.

IMPORTANT TO

Capitalists, Speculators, Quarry Owners, Mining Agents and others.

⟶ Particulars and Plan ⟵

OF SALE OF ALL THE

VALUABLE FREEHOLD

Slate Quarry, Copper Mine & Farm

"DOL-EVAN-GETHIN"

BETTER KNOWN AS

"DOLGETH,"

COMPRISING IN ALL

An area of 25a. 1r. 34p. or thereabouts,

OF ARABLE AND PASTURE LAND,

Upon a portion of which stands the Dolgeth Slate Quarry and Copper Mine, together with the Machinery, Plant, Furniture, and other effects thereon,

WHICH

MESSRS.

W. DEW & SON

ARE INSTRUCTED TO

OFFER FOR SALE BY PUBLIC AUCTION,

AT THE

SPORTSMAN HOTEL, PORTMADOC,

On Saturday, Nov. 21st, 1896,

At ONE o'clock in the Afternoon (Subject to the Chester and North Wales Public Sale Conditions and to certain Special Conditions of Sale to be then produced).

Copies of these PARTICULARS with PLAN, may be obtained of Messrs. NEEDHAM, PARKINSON, SLACK & NEEDHAM, Solicitors, 10, York Street, Manchester; at the principal Hotels in the District; at the Auctioneers' Institute, 57, Chancery Lane, London, W.C.; or of the AUCTIONEERS, Wellfield, Bangor, and Trinity Square, Llandudno. A copy of the Conditions of Sale may be inspected at the offices of the said Solicitors and Auctioneers.

J. R. BROWN, PRINTER, &c., "MINERVA" PRINTING WORKS, HIGH STREET, BANGOR.

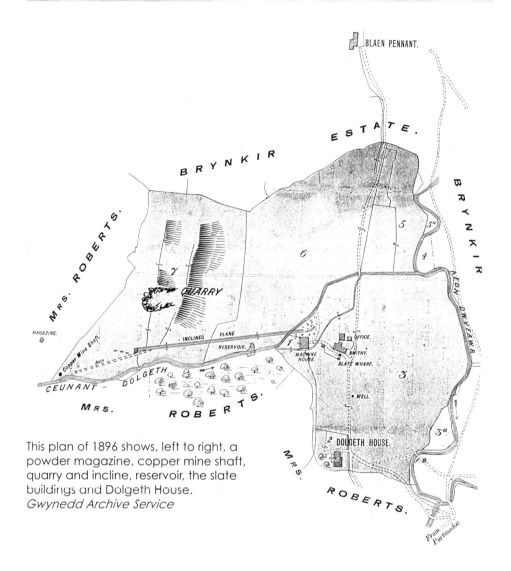

This plan of 1896 shows, left to right, a powder magazine, copper mine shaft, quarry and incline, reservoir, the slate buildings and Dolgeth House.
Gwynedd Archive Service

a 'Brittain [Britten] Pan for Gold Crushing and amalgamating, and small stamps, 3 heads and gear'. But such machinery had nothing to do with slate, and may well have been the legacy of some bygone enterprise locally, or at the site itself.[17c]

A recent visit confirmed the suspicions of earlier activity, for the gable end of the roofless mill could be seen partly standing on an older wall supporting a waterwheel for driving a crusher, presumably to treat copper ore from the shaft high in the crags above. The pit measured about 29ft x 2ft 6in and the wheel's new role was to power the slate-dressing machinery via spur gears and an overhead shaft running the length of the building. The slate episode dates from the 1870s, but absence of waste both from the crushing rolls and mill tells the usual story. [17d]

As to mining, some rich copper-pyrites on a lump of banded shale and calcite was found in the Ceunant stream, but according to the local farmer the shaft was waterfilled; he had never seen the adit shown on the plan. In short, the evidence might suggest a series of ventures, firstly a copper trial, then an attempt to cash in on the gold manias of the 1850s and '60s, and finally slate, all of which turned out a failure. Possibly, the gold machinery had some connection with the Brynkir Gold Syndicate which failed in 1894, and may explain the sale of two years later.

Finally, the empty shell of Dolgeth House deserves a mention. It is a mystery. Clearly uninhabited for generations and perhaps even before the sale of 1896 when it still boasted a greenhouse and roses, it was once a grand double-fronted residence in the early Victorian style, much more suited to a London suburb than the wilds of Snowdonia. I suspected this was a clue to its origins, coming out of the pockets of shareholders who put their faith in an adventure of which no records remain, and this has subsequently been confirmed.[17e] What dreams of grandeur did those walls embrace, all soon to vanish like ghosts at cockcrow, as if they had never been?

The final mine in Cwm Pennant is on the whole well documented. It is on a high amphitheatre at the very head of the valley and began as **BLAEN-Y-PENNANT** (541505) an apt name later discarded in favour of **CWMDWYFOR**.

When the Mining Company of Wales took possession in 1850, lodes of copper and lead had been 'opened by poor men to an average depth of 7 or 8 fathoms . . . but want of system and machinery to command water, caused the works to be suspended'.

Few developments ensued, and the mine subsequently seems to have lain idle until energetically taken up by the Cwmdwyfor Copper & Silver-Lead Mining Co. in the autumn of 1868. The managing director was Thomas Harvey of Bryn-y-Mor, Merioneth, but the four other directors had London addresses. The nominal capital was £12,000 and to raise the money extravagant claims were made – 'The extraordinary richness of the ores, the advantageous position of the lodes for working inexpensively, and the magnitude of the lodes themselves all tend to exhibit one of the most inviting investments in copper and lead which has probably ever been offered to the public in this country'.[18]

But the public not being easily led, Harvey was obliged to find £500 out of his own pocket for further advertising to launch the scheme.[19] Progress was slow, and in spite of less accessible mines elsewhere in the county, its isolation provided a useful excuse for delays.

At this time the 3ft gauge Gorseddau tramway ran from Porthmadog to the Gorseddau quarries a few miles down the valley, and in 1872 an Act authorised conversion of the line to 2ft gauge for locomotive use and to convey passengers. Powers were granted for an extension to the Prince of Wales slate quarry, near Cwmdwyfor, with a branch to the mine itself via an inclined plane.[20]

Supported by George Henwood a well known mining engineer, Harvey and the other directors seized upon these intended developments with relish at a meeting in June 1872. Harvey brought a sample of lead-ore from the mine weighing 160lb, and he asserted that one lode had been proved for 176ft, running at 3-5 tons of ore fathom for much of its length. It was claimed that dividends only awaited the new line, and that the mine's value now amounted to fully £50,000 on the market. With these carrots a thousand unallocated shares were thereupon issued.[19]

In January 1874 Captain N.C. Morcom took over from a Captain Roberts as manager, and at the end of the year the railway was within a mile of the mine. Underground, north and south crosscuts had revealed two lead lodes and six copper lodes within 74 yards 'all yielding payable ore'.

Joseph Jewell subsequently became manager, and early in 1876 he reported the tramway incline and drum completed and working well. De Wintons of Caernarvon had in hand an ore-crusher to be driven by a waterwheel already on the mine, and various buildings were under construction. At the July A.G.M. the incline was described as 255 yards long with two lines of rails, and 226 yards of track extended to the dressing floor.[21] Since the destinies of the mine and the Gorseddau Tramway were so interlinked an intimacy existed between the managements, and G .1. Gray became secretary to both concerns.

Stewart's shaft was sinking for a 20 fathom level, but at 18 fathoms the strata changed from trap-rock to clay-slate, throwing the lode north. About 18 tons of lead-ore had been sold since the line opened, but an adit driven 32 fathoms to cut the lodes 50 fathoms deep was not being proceeded with. The reason for its abandonment became painfully clear at a special general meeting held on 20th September 1876, when the board admitted to being absolutely without funds, and in debt to the tune of £1,120.[22] Furthermore, a report submitted by D.C. Davies, F.G.S. of Oswestry held out little optimism.[23]

A few weeks later the company suffered a further blow from a long and amusing letter in the *Mining World*

Some companies, like man himself, are born to trouble, as the sparks fly upward. They are launched in a sea of difficulties, and the waters never seem to subside until they have engulphed them. . . . I do the Cwm Dwyfor Company no injustice when I say that from its very birth till the present time it has been in all the throes of financial agony. Its career has been unenlivened by a single ray of hope, and it is hard to attribute its present existence to other than the rhetorical flourishes of its management and the sanguine reports of its officials...'

The writer went on to disclose how Harvey himself had sold the mine to the company for not less than £10,000 in cash, and his apparently magnanimous gesture with the £500 came to light merely as an expedient to keep the venture buoyant enough to secure the money.[24]

Later in 1876 an extraordinary general meeting decided to wind up, and G.J. Gray became the liquidator. The assets were to be taken up by an ostensibly new venture, the Cwmdwyfor Mining Co. Ltd. John Roberts of Simdde Dylluan issued a report drawing similarities between the two mines and expressing faith in sinking deeper.[25] The true situation however, had not escaped a correspondent to the mining press 'I am sorry that success does not attend this enterprise', he wrote, 'because great preseverance has been bestowed upon it, at least in the share department. . . . Had a Coroner's jury sat upon the body of the old concern, its verdict must have been "died from natural causes" '[26]

Nonetheless money was somehow raised, and in April 1877 Captain Jewel reopened the workings with the intention of driving a 19 fathom level from Stewart's Shaft to cut other lodes.

Results were disappointing, and in July 1878 the board announced plans to abandon Cwmdwyfor in favour of a lead mine in Cardiganshire known as Brynarian or Cardigan Bay Consols.[27] How an old and exhausted property 50 miles away which had lately brought three companies to ruin could exert such a spell is incomprehensible; but the decision was taken, and Cwmdwyfor came up for auction in November 1879. We may suspect the last traffic over the line comprised the materials and plant including a 35ft x 4ft waterwheel, two winching drums 10ft x 6ft and 3ft x 7ft, incline rollers, double crab-winch and various other items.[28]

Cwmdwyfor's enviable distinction as the only copper mine in Snowdonia to achieve direct rail communication with a port availed it little, except by the credit fostered in the anticipation, for the entire output hardly justified a single train.

The old tramway makes a convenient and fitting approach to the mine and can be reached by a steep path ascending from the end of the Cwm Pennant road. The path meets the line near its junction with the route to the Prince of Wales slate quarry. The incline is gained after about half a mile, and is complete apart from a bridge over the Afon Dwyfor. The drumhouse has a rough dividing wall which is apparently a later addition. Beyond, the trackbed leads to the mine where two buildings are on the right, opposite a massive masonry wheelpit (41ft x 5ft 9in) and crusherhouse alongside. Further over is a terrace of ruined barracks.

The site layout is of considerable interest. Conspicuous features are the remnants of three parallel rows of stone pillars, and the purposes of which are not altogether clear, leading from the crusherhouse and wheelpit to a pumping shaft. Possibly one row supported launders for the wheel, another guided flat-rods for pumping, and the third carried a tramway to convey ore to the mill. On the other side of the wheelpit was a drawing machine (winding drum), but with such an arrangement the derivation of motion for the flat-rods is difficult to envisage. The crusherhouse is robustly constructed, the south wall being heavily buttressed, perhaps as result of structural weakness because it was added on at a late date, and not integral with the wheelpit.

There are also numerous grassgrown trials on the outcrops of several lodes. At the time of my first visit in 1952 tons of muddy grey sulphide ores (pyrrhotite?) were lying about, of which little now remains. Altogether an absorbing valley for the industrial archaeologist and historian, in which there were even trials for asbestos, to the north of Moel Lefn.

Beyond the mountains north of Cwmdwyfor is the Nantlle Vale, which has produced much of the copper raised in Snowdonia. The lodes outcropping in the cliff-like side of the valley must have been early discovered, and probably the oldest working was **DRWSYCOED** (545534) which King Edward I reputedly visited in 1284.

In the 18th century an interested party was Lord Powys, but even though his influence on developments proved minimal the interlude is not without significance because of the light thrown on the intrigues and infighting that so often accompanied such ventures.

Well known in London society, Powys had earlier realised a fortune from his lead mines at Llangynog, all of which had gone in settling debts. Attempts to maintain this income by leasing Esgairmwyn in Cardiganshire were meeting with little reward, and we may suppose an element bordering on despair turned attention to North Wales. In this, he was prey to numerous scheming employees and hirelings including Griffith Pryce, John Griffiths and John Paynter, of whom the latter had been agent to the Penrhyn Estate from 1736 to 1744, becoming manager of Esgairmwyn in 1756.

The following somewhat testy note illustrates the problems of controlling and

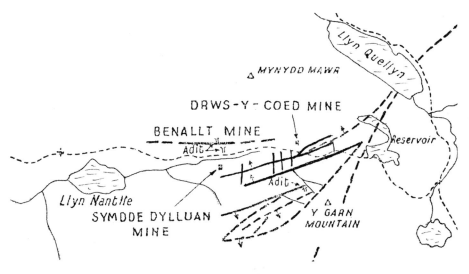

The mineral lodes at Drwsycoed, Simdde Dylluan and Benallt.   *S. Dawson Ware*

even comprehending events at a distance in a land remote as the moon, to say nothing of interpreting leases which before the days of accurate maps were often very difficult to define.[2]

Griffiths,   Albemarle Street. May 10th 1768
Enclosed is the Plan you sent me in February 1765 of the Waste of Cwmdu, with notes of Reference to explain it; and I have just now been comparing with it the description you gave me of it t'other day with your observations but I cannot make the matter out, so far as to say that I thoroughly understand the whole. I desire therefore you will take the enclosed Plan and consider it well and then return it to me; adding such names of Mountains and Places now contained there in as were then omitted; together with such notes of reference also, as may make me clearly acquainted with all the Material Parts and Circumstances you meant to inform me of. In your letter which brought this Plan to me you describe the Waste of Cwmdu to be of great Extent; and to have different Parts of it distinguished by different names; (viz) Mynydd fawr Cilgwyn etc. etc. etc. In a few days you shall have another letter from me with other instructions about other Points that were mentioned lately in my discourse with you. I am etc. etc.

Powis

The waste of Cwmdu encompassed a huge area west of Rhyd-ddu though not the profitable Drwsycoed, which belonged to the Assheton Smith family. This unfortunate circumstance could be rectified according to Griffith Pryce, who wrote to Powys in February 1770 claiming that a deed or grant of land including Drwsycoed and Aberglaslyn would be found among the papers of Powys' grandfather – an assertion which from the grovelling tone of the letter originated more with an eye to currying favour than from any basis in reality.[3] Pryce went on to report 'about 2 yards wide of Liver Coulor Copper on the west above Drwsycoyd', but little or nothing more was heard of his Lordship's ambition in the district.

Drwsycoed was in fact hard at work at this time. It formed the eastern section of a group of lodes running more or less along the valley containing quartz, pyrrhotite, copper and iron-pyrites, blende and galena, with valuable enrichments near slides or cross-courses. According to the late S. Dawson Ware, the ore sometimes ran 20% metallic copper in deposits up to 24ft thick.

By the mid-18th century the mine had developed considerably. Part was below the present road with the more important area where the lodes outcropped on the steep scarp of the mountain high above. The state of the workings is given by this extract from a report dated August 1760. [4]

'The works in the Coppermines of Drwsycoed are distinguished by the lower Vein or Wood Vein, the Middle Vein, and the main Drift or highest Vein –
These several Works seem to lay in One Vein or Direction pointing from North East to South West but more inclining to the East and West –
A considerable Quantity of Ore has been got at each of these Works but the most at the Highest which has been therefore called the main Drift –
The ore in the Wood Vein at the first opening thereof seemed to be the best Ore and it was observed that in the other Veins the lower the Ore lay the better it was –
As to the lower Vein or Wood Vein –
The first discovery of Ore at this place was at the bottom of the Mountain so low that a drain was cut to carry off the Water and a Shaft has been since sunk Twelve yards Deep, with an Intent to fix an Engine for pumping up the Water, and the Ore continued all the Depth of

Between Drwsycoed and Simdde Dylluan, these 18th century miners' cottages survive as ruins under a high cliff, where for most of the year the sun never shone.
David Bick

This 54 inch diameter pit-head wheel, probably from the engine shaft at Drwsycoed, was unearthed during site reclamation and is now at Sygun. The spokes are wrought iron, with a cast-iron rim.
David Bick

the Shaft – but on making a Drift towards the West which has been carried on about 12 yards there was little or no Ore in the last 5 yds. and therefore a stop has been put to this work about 2 yrs. As to the Middle Vein or Work –

Since the discovery of the Ore in this place which appeared at the Surface of the Rock towards the East and Sunk downwards, several drains or levels have been cut across the Rock into the Vein of the Ore and Drifts made in the Vein which have cut out to the surface towards the East but a breast of Ore is left towards the West or main drift, but seems to be only fit for the Stampers.

As to the Highest Vein or main Drift –

Several drains or levels have been cut across the Rock to the Ore in this place and two other levels still lower are now driving, but are not yet carried on to the Vein.

The Ore in this main Drift does not extend above 12 yds in length from East to West but being High in the Rock cuts out both ways. This Drift has been sunk about 20 yds shelving as the rock shelves and there is Ore at the floor or bottom.'

The Rev. Richard Farrington, rector of Llangybi, acted as agent for a few years prior to 31st March 1770, and upon his death in 1772 his wife inherited $^1/_3$ part of his shares and profits in the venture.[5] Farrington's father-in-law was a Mr. Richardson of Chester who worked the mine on a large scale at this period, before coming off in the end a loser. In 1781 Pennant referred to this interlude as 'considerable adventures for copper of the yellow kind, and in the rocks were sometimes found some very thin laminae of the native metal'. The mine had been abandoned before 1777, and a few men were set to work in 1792, in attempts to encourage a new company to take up the lease.

On 31st July 1813, the antiquarian Richard Fenton passed this way from Beddgelert and descended into the vale 'under a very high and broken mountain whose bowels seem well stored with Copper Ore, at the base of which by the ruins now appearing, there appears to have been a large old Work, now revived further on . . .'. Whether the new activity referred to Drwsycoed or the neighbouring Simdde Dylluan is not clear.

An occasion for celebration arose in 1829, for the account books reveal 'expenses for dinner to the miners per T.A. Smith's order, £12.0.0'. The same source also gives the cost of making two horsewhims – £10.0.6d.

Thomas Assheton Smith the elder died during the previous year, and his huge estates passed to his son of the same name, about whom a few words may not come amiss.[6] Thomas Assheton Smith (1776-1858) from his early years practically lived in the saddle, and became England's most enthusiastic and relentless fox-hunter, to the point of obsession.

A friend of the Duke of Wellington and R.I. Murchison the geologist (also a fox-hunter), Assheton Smith was also a pioneer of steam-yachts, which were no toys, but vessels up to 700 tons displacement. The first, *Menai,* was completed in 1830, but the innovation incurred the displeasure of the Royal Yacht Club, from which he resigned. Three subsequent vessels built in 1844-6 were each called *Fire Queen.* The 1848 locomotive constructed by Horlick & Co. which for long worked the Dinorwic slate traffic, bore the same name, and we may suspect that Assheton Smith had a hand in the choice if not the design, of this eccentric machine. It is preserved at Penrhyn Castle Museum.

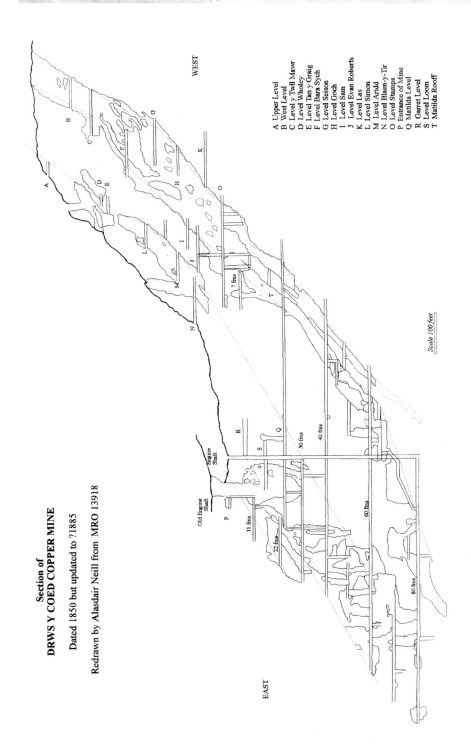

Section of
DRWS Y COED COPPER MINE

Dated 1850 but updated to ?1885

Redrawn by Alasdair Neill from MRO 13918

A Upper Level
B West Level
C Level y Twll Mawr
D Level Wholey
E Level Tan y Graig
F Level Bara Sych
G Level Selson
H Level Goch
I Level Sam
J Level Evan Roberts
K Level Las
L Level Simon
M Level Aridd
N Level Blaen-y-Tir
O Level Stamps
P Entrance of Mine
Q Matilda Level
R Garret Level
S Level Loom
T Matilda Rooff

Scale 100 feet

WEST

EAST

He also introduced a novel form of railway at his residences, along which dishes passed from the kitchens. At Vaynol (near Port Dinorwic) 'the train arriving with its savoury load opened a trapdoor at the end of the dining-room; this closed of itself immediately after the admission of the course, and thus no inconvenience arose from the smell of cooking which frequently penetrates open doors and passages in the largest houses. The weight of the empty dishes going down, as in the case of the slate waggons at Llanberris, brought upon the platform within the dining-room by means of diminutive connecting ropes, the hot and smoking trucks coming up. This process, if not the only one of the kind in England, was at all events invented and introduced entirely by Mr. Smith'. A system, surely, to warm the heart of every railway enthusiast.

Whether Assheton Smith took any particular interest in his mines is unlikely. They were in any case of little account compared to the Dinorwic quarries, which towards the end of his life were alone bringing in £30,000 clear profit a year, at a time when the average labouring man existed as best he could on ten shillings (50p) a week.

Returning now to Drwsycoed, something of its potential was revealed during the years 1821-40, when it sold ores amounting to over 6,000 tons to Swansea. In August 1830 Joseph Jones, late of Amlwch, took control on behalf of Assheton Smith and a marked rise in output followed.[7] This had been assisted by the Nantlle Railway, opened in 1828, a horse-operated tramway of 3ft 6ins gauge to the quay at Caernarvon. In the first six months of 1831, 522 tons of ore went over the line, of which some 100 tons were shipped on 1st January to St. Helens on board the *Cathrine*.[8] During the whole year, 629 tons were sold to Swansea, rising to 916 tons in 1832 to that destination alone.

The rapid increase in output may have resulted from reopening the old east-end workings below the road, for this is the area marked 'mineworks' on a plan drawn up for an 1836 lease.[9] The plan also shows 'old minehouses and yards' occupying about half an acre at the western boundary of the sett where empty shells of cottages still stand south of the road.

The 21 year lease concerned an agreement between Assheton Smith and Richard Griffith of Dublin together with seven merchants from Liverpool, and gave authority to erect pumping engines. Furthermore, it stipulated that Llanberis and Clogwyn Coch, also on Assheton Smith's land, should also be kept at work. During the 1830s and later the three mines operated together, the same account books and ledgers serving all.

In 1853 Richard Griffiths & partners obtained a further lease of 21 years but trouble with drainage arose in 1857 and there was talk of a steam engine; at the other extreme, reliance on water-power brought the works to a stand two years later due to a drought.[10] Thomas Assheton Smith died in 1858 without issue, and his estates in Wales passed to his sister's grandson, G.W. Duff Assheton Smith.

The company ceased activities in 1874 and a publicly owned venture took over. On 2nd June 1875 G.W.D. Assheton Smith granted a lease to William Forster who had been associated with the previous working. In the next March Forster sold the lease to the Drws y Coed Copper Mining Co. Ltd., newly formed with £10,000 nominal capital in £10 shares. Apart from Forster who lived at Nantwich, the directors included R.S. Johnson, William Fairbairn Hall, colliery engineer and James Monks

These ancient stopes reveal the lode where it crosses the road near Old Engine Shaft.
David Bick

colliery owner, with John Cameron Swan acting as secretary, all of County Durham.
[11] How these men from the north-east became involved is not clear. Thomas Lewis was agent in 1879, with only 18 men employed altogether. Drwsycoed proved only a shadow of its former self, with annual output rarely exceeding 200 tons of ore, falling to zero in 1887.

In 1894 Mineral Estates Ltd. took over at a period of rock-bottom copper prices, and two years later returned 1668 tons of poor ore 'obtained in making experiments', of which unfortunately no details survive.[13] The miners never much exceeded a dozen, and the attempt ended in bankruptcy six years after it began.

Before 1901 a large new mill was built east of Engine Shaft on a higher level, and from an old photograph it appears that an inclined railway between the road and launders to the pumping wheel brought ore from the shaft to the mill.

Drwsycoed does not figure in the Mines Inspector's Reports for the years 1902-16, but according to local information a German company employed a hundred people from 1906 and 1911, with a Mr Berrisford managing and Captain James Hughes in charge underground. The ore was heated in retorts to remove the sulphur and leached with sulphuric acid, copper metal being obtained by electrolytic deposition – a very interesting and unusual process. Sufficient gold was obtained to provide a tiepin for Dr. J.C. Butterfield, the chemist.[12] It is said that some of the stopes were big enough to engulf a row of houses; in earlier days ore went cross-country to Caernarvon on the backs of mules, and rocks were split by expansion of quick-lime rammed in boreholes and left to work all night.

The next revival came during World War I, when in 1917 the Mining Corporation of Great Britain reopened the mine together with Simdde Dylluan or Talysarn to the west, and again only a handful of men were employed.[13] Since the two did not connect underground, no great economy in the working might have been anticipated, except perhaps in dressing, which took place at Drwsycoed. The ore passed through a stone-breaker, rolls and Green's jigs, the fines being treated on a Wilfley Table. [14] Mining was largely confined to the 56 fathom level at Talysarn, the last year being 1920. The output did not amount to more than two or three hundred tons altogether.

The total recorded produce of Drwsycoed is some 13,000 tons of ore, but is certainly a great underestimate; double this quantity might be nearer the mark. The works were extensive, and both from an old plan and by inspection are revealed as a veritable rabbit-warren, reminiscent in places underground of Parys Mine, Anglesey. The plan, dated 1845, was corrected up to 1885 by John Roberts, and is an exceedingly instructive document.[15]

It appears that the bottom or 80 fathom level had been begun if not completed before 1845, and the ore to the east was cut out by a crosscourse dipping at a shallow angle in the same direction. The 60 extended almost 100 fathoms easterly to the crosscourse from Engine Shaft and the 80, somewhat further. There were extensive stopes right up to the surface.

About 25 fathoms south-east of Engine Shaft was Old Engine Shaft, 12 fathoms deep, beneath an archway constructed in the retaining wall of the main road. The former shaft is now obscured.

It is probably true to say that the bulk of the workings were to the south of the road beneath the steep escarpment of the mountain from which ore was readily removable by adits, the deepest of which was Level Stamps, now blocked just inside. This emerged under the road where a ruined building and wheelpit mark the remnants of an important centre of dressing operations. This adit probably dates from the late 18th century.

Many of the levels were low and narrow, of somewhat oval section in which wheelbarrows without legs were used, known as 'berfa hurch' or sow barrows.[16] On the mountainside are extensive opencuts with a number of adits including Level Goch and beneath it Level Las, the latter still leading to labyrinthine workings. To attempt to corellate these various features with the description of the mine in 1760 as previously noted, is an absorbing exercise. The whole hillside is a mass of scree and iron-stained waste, hand-cobbed by women and children working long hours for a pittance, with low dry-stone walls to save them from the worst of the weather. A number of these little work-houses complete with stone benches are conspicuous, though hardly visible from the road. Whether they were roofed is doubtful, and only a moment there in driving wind and rain demonstrates very forcibly the rigours of an 18th century mineworker's life.

The orebodies dipped eastwards, and little or nothing appears to have been found below the vicinity of Level Stamps, whilst to the west the old bottoms were much higher. Whether further courses of ore exist at lower horizons is of course, an intriguing possibility.

In earlier times the whole process of mining at Drwsycoed and elsewhere relied on

Drwsycoed in 1978. The massive stone pier is hollow and was part of the water supply to the 40ft wheel. The archway beyond carries the road over Old Engine Shaft. The wooden pipe, now lost, is probably a rising main from the 18th century.   *David Bick*

manual and animal labour for pumping, winding, crushing and ore-dressing, but in the 19th century waterpower to a great extent relieved such onerous duties, and enabled output greatly to increase. There are traces of a wheelpit for a 40ft diameter pumping wheel and the nearby tall rectangular stone pier supported launders conveying water. The pier is hollow for by-passing water to adjust the power output, a feature which one author has mistaken for a feed to an undershot wheel. These hollow columns, whether of wood or stone, were appropriately named 'cafn gwyllt' (wild spout).[17]

In recent years the Welsh Development Agency has landscaped much of Drwsycoed 'to improve the environment', but at what cost to the industrial archaeology is best left unsaid.

At the head of the valley, Llyn Dywarchen was raised in level to serve as a reservoir and Llyn Bwlch-y-moch just to the north was later built to augment the reserves, but it is now dry. A leat contouring the north-eastern slopes of Y Garn conveyed water over the bwlch towards Drwsycoed. Evidence on the ground suggests it was later diverted into Llyn Dywarchen, and the channel, paved on steeper portions to prevent scouring, still carries a good flow of mountain water – one of the very few mining watercourses still operating in Wales. At the end of the 19th century a further source was added in the form of a high-level leat contouring the rugged mountains passing through several tunnels south of Drwsycoed and descending by pipeline.[18] The course of the leat and positions of the reservoirs are clearly shown on the $2^1/_2$ inch/mile (1:25,000) Ordnance map.

Good mines excite an intensive search for others in the vicinity, and much prospecting resulted on copper and lead lodes in the mountains behind Drwsycoed. Trial adits bear witness to these attempts, and similar efforts were made in the valley east of the mine, but without much success.

To the west of Drwsycoed the same lodes were worked at **SIMDDE DYLLUAN** or Owl's Chimney, also known as **TALYSARN** (543533) – a mine working in the 18th century if not before. [19] The Geological Survey has recorded that the lodes were four in number, and separated each from the other by about 14ft of slate. No.2 was the richest, and in width up to 30ft at Drwsycoed.[20] The influence of cross-courses on ore deposition was of paramount importance, as will be noticed shortly. In the 1830s the mine belonged to Richard Garnons, the owner of Dorothea slate quarry, and sold ore at Swansea almost continuously from 1826 to 1840, exceeding 4000 tons in total. In 1832 no less than 1032 tons were sold, this making almost the highest annual recorded sale of any copper mine in Snowdonia.

A private company worked Simdde Dylluan in the mid-19th century from two shafts about 100 fathoms apart, near the foot of the escarpment. In 1863 John Petherick acted as manager, with Captain Thomas Julian as chief agent, when the workings were down to a 70 fathom level. According to a Government report, wages were high due to demand for labour in the local slate quarries, but 'some of the men live at Carnarvon, and these sleep in a house adjoining the office which is much too small, very dirty and badly ventilated'.[21]

William Stevens was listed as manager in 1868 with John Roberts subsequently taking the position. In 1873 Captain Sandoe of D'Eresby Mountain mine near Llanrwst supervised sinking a new shaft near the western end of the workings. The ground proved excessively hard, and the objective had not been completed before financial difficulties arose.

Roberts also had associations with D'Eresby Mountain, and perhaps to revive interest in Simdde Dylluan, wrote a long account to the mining press which threw some light on the nature of the deposits.[22] According to his evidence a fault or cross-slide had cut off the Drwsycoed lode and thrown it down to the level of the valley. In both mines the chief deposits of copper ore were associated with slides of a fairly shallow inclination, and made good upon them, but never beneath. Very rich carbonas had been discovered, 5-10 fathoms high and 3-4 fathoms wide. These slides were called by the miners 'y mam copr' or mother of copper.[23] Roberts added that large amounts of iron-pyrites occurred on the outcrops of the lodes where they were most productive, calling to mind the old German saying 'there is no lode like that, which wears an iron hat'.

Work seems to have ceased in 1877 but revived in January 1880 under the Carnarvon Copper Co. Ltd., with a nominal capital of £20,000. The promoters were

Watson Brothers, mine owners and stockbrokers of 1, St. Michaels Alley, Cornhill, London. The directors included Samuel Whitfield Dawkes, Joseph Yelloly Watson, Napoleon Frederick Watson and W.H.H. Watson, and the secretary was C.B. Parry.[24]

The Watsons, Roberts and Sandoe were also involved in lead mines near Llanrwst, including Clementina (which boasted a 60ft waterwheel and practically no water to drive it), D'Eresby Mountain, D'Eresby Consols and Aberllyn, none of which were doing any good, at least for the shareholders. Thus, via Roberts and Sandoe, the hand of the Watsons in the late working of Simdde Dylluan may be suspected. At all events their interest was now certain, and came across in promotional announcements with the usual half-truths and distortions that typified the ethics and hastened the decline of British mining in the latter part of the 19th century.

Notwithstanding the failure of the previous attempt, it was implied that 900 tons of ore were returned within recent years but suspension had been decided until better times came. Copper prices were in reality now lower than ever, but the fact was not revealed. The proprietor, William Stevens, had accepted £12,000 in shares for the mine and Talymignedd-isaf farm leaving the balance available for investors.[24]

The proposal consisted of driving the 90 fathom level west to communicate with Garnons' Shaft to open up new ground and improve ventilation. The lode in the 90 was supposedly different from the 80 at Garnons' which the promoters considered auspicious due to the anticipated enrichment at the junction. Pumping out both workings proved a long and tiresome task, but there was good progress at first as can be gathered from Roberts' report dated 26th February 1880.

> Since we commenced about a month ago, we have made and fixed 190 fathoms of pulley-stands for flat-rods, made a new stand and box for balance-bob, and a new wooden connecting rod at the top of the engine shaft; repaired the large water-wheel, which is now just like new; made and fixed a new horizontal angle-bob, put about another dozen pieces in the iron rods, and several other things too many to mention. We started the pumps yesterday morning, which are forking the water at the rate of 2 fathoms per day. We have now to repair the pulley-stands of the winding machine, and new backing to put in the water-wheel belonging to it....

Unfortunately, developments at the new engine shaft were less satisfactory; the pumps proved inadequate and to compound the difficulties the rods of the top lift broke and jammed. The expedient was then adopted of baling out the water in a barrel with a horse-whim to a depth of 14 fathoms – a slow enough undertaking but according to Roberts, quicker than the pumps.

Meanwhile a new lode attracted attention at Talymignedd in the western part of the sett and a little exploration was done. By July 1880 both workings had been drained to shaft bottoms and the footway repaired in the old mine (Garnons'). In driving west by six men at the 90 fathom level the ground proved desperately hard quartzite, with 3 feet per week being the best rate of progress attained. At surface, a capstan and shears were erected for lowering bigger pumps and removing pitwork from Garnons' to the new engine-shaft in anticipation of a large volume of water when the 90 holed through into the sump below the 80 (see section).

In December 1880 a winze below the 36 fathom level at Cae-y-groes (Golden

Venture Shaft) revealed good ore, and a rise commenced in the 46 to meet it. By the spring fortunes appeared brighter, with a 6 to 8 inch leader of rich ore in the lode in the 90. However, it was soon disordered by a slide, although in July 1881 was reported up to $2^{1}/_{2}$ft wide, nearly solid, and looking splendid. In the same month came the long-awaited event of holing through at the 90 fathom level, which signalled much improved ventilation and in theory at least, the commencement of major returns.

At the A.G.M. a year later with Watson in the chair, it was admitted that sales during the previous 12 months had only amounted to £1,036, which Roberts attributed to want of proper dressing machinery. But in the autumn work below the 90 ceased, and the futility of the grand object became increasingly apparent. However, as a kind of consolation prize, a little ore was scraped together during the winter from the 20, 36 and 70 fathom levels at Garnons', the 46 at Golden Venture, the 80 east, and above the 90. But returns proved elusive after a gale blew down the launders to one of the wheels, with no funds available for repairs.

The 1883 A.G.M. revealed a sorry spectacle. Only £2,710 worth of ore amounting to 229 tons had been sold in the past year, and Watson thrust Roberts forward as a scapegoat to explain to shareholders the reason for their disappointment. An attempt to increase the capital failed, and Simdde Dylluan complete with all plant and equipment came up for sale in May 1884. The ore had been high-grade, but patchy and insufficient to pay. Thumbing through the old reports, one gains the impression of lodes cut to ribbons by slides and faults, and miners confused as to what they followed, even supposing a lode at all.

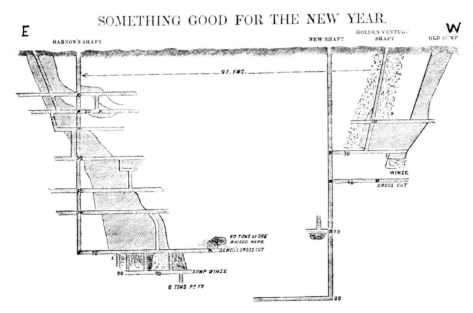

This section of Simdde Dylluan appeared as part of the Watson Brothers promotion in *The Mining Journal.*

In 1890 John Thomas, auctioneer of Caernarvon was listed as owner, and a few were employed at surface and underground until about 1895. The Nantlle Vale Copper Mining Co. took over in 1900 and returned 74 tons before fading away after a year or two.

In 1907 the Talysarn Copper Mines employed 12 men underground, rising to 35 in 1909, and some of the ore exceeded 20% copper. However, the quantity fell short

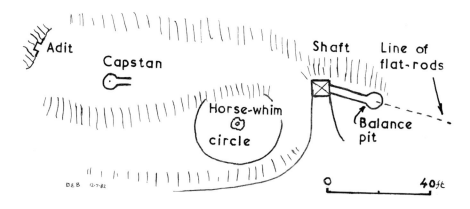

A sketch showing the remaining features at Garnon's Shaft.

This view of New Shaft at Simdde Dylluan (Talysarn) was taken in 1930 by Russell Bayles from just west of the gateway to Talymignedd Farm.   *Clwyd RO*

of a profit and a liquidator was appointed in 1914. The last revival came in association with Drwsycoed, as previously mentioned. Simdde Dylluan could claim the deepest workings in Snowdonia, in a winze sunk 20 fathoms under the 96, or a total of 116 fathoms from surface.[25]

As to the state of the mine today, the area alongside the road has been levelled, destroying several buildings and the new engine shaft from which later developments were mainly conducted. However the rocky escarpment is riddled with workings, and at its foot near a huge white boulder is Garnons' Shaft, now blocked, with a nearby horsewhim circle and stone pedestal bearing. On a higher level is a shallow masonry-lined pit for housing the capstan to handle heavy equipment in the shaft, and the course of the line of flat-rods is traceable for some distance westward.

In the rocks above a gateway and cattle-grid are further workings including a horsewhim circle and a deep vertical shaft, but correlation with the appended plan is not very easy. Further west a dingle below the road reveals two waterwheel pits, the larger for pumping. These wheels were unusual, being fed in parallel rather than in series, indicating a fairly abundant water supply; an old postcard of the Nantlle Valley showed both with the mine head-frame in the background. Altogether a rewarding site for the industrial archaeologist.

Across the valley a number of adits dotted over the mountainside signify **BENALLT** (536535). Its history is worth including, and serves to illustrate the ease by which capital could be raised in the 1870s for anything remotely resembling a lead mine, following the success of Roman Gravels and Tankerville in Shropshire and particularly Van, near Llanidloes, which for a time became the greatest lead producer in Europe.[26] (Benallt should not be confused with a manganese mine of the same name, near Aberdaron.)

In 1845 Benallt amounted to merely a level 110 yds long, cutting a vein 3ft wide with 'copper, mundic and black jack' – the two latter denoting iron-pyrites and zinc-blende.[27] Twenty-five years later several Londoners, having recently purchased the sett, promoted the Pen'Allt Silver-Lead Mining Co. Directors included W.G. Craig of Surbiton, John Dixon, and W. H. Bond of Lewisham. Favourable reports were received from J. Frazer of Caernarvon, Thomas Glanville late of North Basset, and Captains Ridge of Llanidloes and Goldsworthy of Camborne.[28] The property contained four lodes, one assaying 101 oz of silver per ton of lead – or so it was claimed.

Money was quickly subscribed and Glanville became manager. Work commenced on Nos. 1, 2, 3 and 4 crosscuts, and by July 1870 an extensive mill near the river had been largely completed. It included a waterwheel and crushing rolls, and a Blake's stone-breaker which for some inexplicable reason was driven by steam. There was also a large building in course of erection to house patent German dressing machinery supplied by George Green of Aberystwyth. A self-acting incline descended from the lowest or No.4 adit to the stone-breaker and further inclines were proposed from other levels. According to a puffing announcement, 'extending from two-thirds the height of the mountain to the water's edge the works will, when in full operation, present a scene of animation and industry not to be equalled in the Principality'.

Investors however, were becoming uneasy in spite of Glanville's repeated assurances of immense quantities of ore awaiting treatment, but all appeared well at a meeting held on site in November 1870; they were able to witness the incline operating and could inspect 'the best and most modern dressing machinery that could be produced'. Nevertheless production did not materialize.

The truth came out in April 1871 when a shareholder in reporting over £3000 expended on machinery, also revealed that Captain Kitto had denounced such outlay as premature.[29] Professor Forbes had condemned the whole venture out of hand, and

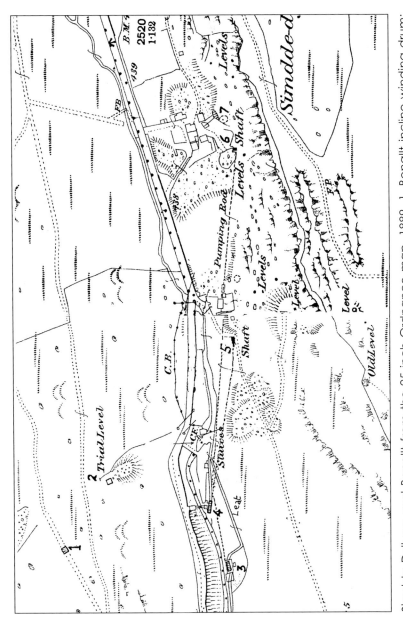

Simdde Dylluan and Benallt from the 25 inch Ordnance map, 1889. 1, Benallt incline winding drum; 2, Benallt deep adit; 3, pumping wheel; 4, pumping and crushing wheel (note bridge to the road); 5, New shaft; 6, Garnon's Shaft; 7, capstan circle.

Glanville would be called upon 'to explain the wonderful discrepancy between his estimates and actual results'.[30] It also transpired that the latter had been dealing in shares, but his embarrassment was spared by the appointment as manager of Robert Casement, late of Laxey Mine, Isle of Man.[31]

Casement quickly summed up the situation, and the best he could accomplish was one ton of concentrate out of 50 tons of ore. Underground, a winze below No.3 adit was about to hole through into No.4, but a general paucity of material rendered the prospects bleak, and legal proceedings were taken out against Frazer for alleged money owing. Much discussion had arisen as to where the ore could have gone to – the machinery providing the favourite scapegoat. Green responded by dryly observing that during 20 years in the business, this was not the first time when ore had mysteriously disappeared after completion of the dressing plant. The company presented a petition to wind up in July 1871 and subsequently the directors were faced with a protracted legal action.

An undertaking more ill-managed and incompetent, not to say fraudulent, could scarcely be conceived, and was precisely the kind of promotion exemplified by the following cautionary words written many years before. 'The uncertain nature of metalliferous mining affords unusual facilities for making unscrupulous misrepresentations, and consequently whenever, through the abundance of money or other favourable causes, the public mind becomes credulous, it admits the grossest mis-statements without examination, and readily consents to pay exorbitant sums for properties which are probably altogether worthless, or at least of but little intrinsic value. Sooner or later, however, the truth is arrived at, and under the influence of a violent reaction, an industry that deserves well is denounced as a delusion, whilst the real circumstances producing the evil are either slurred over or forgotten.'[32]

Notwithstanding the debacle, the directors, or most of them, must have done pretty well, for hardly had Pen'Allt ceased activity when they coolly promoted the Great Mountain Silver-Lead Mining Co. to acquire the site for £2000.[33] Captain J. Frazer the new manager, had figured behind the scenes of the old concern, and as if to redeem the sterility of the venture, made much of a supposed discovery of umber, a paint pigment claimed to be worth up to £14 per ton. In July 1872 he announced an obvious economy by driving the crusher from the waterwheel, and at the second A.G.M. in February 1873 a few tons of galena and blende from No.4 adit were ready for market.[34] A deep adit recently begun, was now the grand object for the future. The chairman admitted to considerable delays and expense due to 'indispensable alterations and repairs to the machinery . . . but we are advised that a few stamps will overcome all difficulties'. George Green had a good reputation, and it would be interesting to know more about this patent German machinery, and whether it really was at fault.

The deep adit reached its objective in August 1874. The lode at depth proved much as before, and the venture ended in Chancery having fared no better than its predecessor. The mine lay idle for many years thereafter, and a report by W. H. Williams, late manager of the Van mines, revealed the little work actually done.[35] In spite of the record, the new century witnessed a further series of fruitless promotions including the following:[36]

Benallt Copper & Lead Mines Ltd.	Registered 1906
Consolidated Zinc & Lead Mines Ltd.	Registered 1917
Mining Corporation of Gt. Britain Ltd	Registered 1878
Nantlle Vale Mineral Leases Ltd.	Registered 1925

According to the prospectus, the Nantlle Vale promoters were H.A. Huntley and J.R. Marsh, both of Cannon St., London, and owners of an option on Drwsycoed, Simdde Dylluan and Benallt complete with all equipment for £20,000. The idea was to work Benallt initially and apply the profits to unwater and develop the others. The plant included three water-wheels, the smallest being of 40 h.p., one of which drove an air-hoist and hammer-drill via an air compressor.

An old mill and a waterwheel were resurrected (presumably at Simdde Dylluan) and electric power installed. There was also an aerial ropeway to convey ore. Although a more improbable scheme could scarcely be imagined, the venture nevertheless survived until 1931 when liabilities exceeding £11,000 brought the long story of mining in the Nantlle valley to an end.

The dumps outside No.4 level reveal a powerful lode, and are composed almost entirely of a brown-weathered mineral which frequently accompanies copper ore in Mid-Wales. This appears to be ankerite, and not sparry iron ore which it much resembles.

The route of the tramway incline leads down under the road, terminating above a hollow which presumably once held the rock-breaker, crusher and waterwheel, if not the steam engine. Though some masonry survives the layout is not at all clear, and neither is the course of the leat. Near the river stand three walls of the Green's dressing mill, measuring about 50ft x 70ft, with a wheelpit alongside. The fourth wall is not shown on the 25 inch map (1889) and perhaps never existed. The contents may have resembled the machinery in Green's later mills, as at Rhoswydol near Machynlleth, described elsewhere.[37]

NANTLLE VALE MINERAL LEASES, LTD.

Directors—H. A. Huntley, *Chairman*; J. R. Marsh; N. Seth-Smith.
Consulting Engineer—A. R. Canning, M.Inst.M.M. Mine Manager—J. H. Jeffers.
Secretary and Offices—C. Jackson, 28, Budge Row, E.C. 4.

Registered—September 14, 1925, to acquire from H. A. Huntley and J. R. Marsh an option to purchase the Drws-y-Coed, Talysarn and Benallt copper-lead and zinc mines in the upper section of the Vale of Nantlle, Carnarvonshire. The consideration for the option was 10,000 fully-paid deferred shares of 1s. each, and £1,000 cash, the latter payable £500 when 2,000 shares have been subscribed and £500 when 4,000 shares have been subscribed. If exercised the consideration for the properties and plant to be £8,000 cash and £12,000 in fully-paid shares in any company formed to work the mines, or £15,000 cash.

Capital—£10,500, in 10,000 ordinary shares of £1 and 10,000 deferred shares of 1s. each; 2,304 ordinary shares are issued and 15s. paid, and all the deferred shares are issued credited as fully paid. In October, 1925, all the ordinary shares were offered for subscription at par. The ordinary shares are entitled to 75 per cent. of profits, the deferred taking the balance. When the ordinary shares have received 100 per cent. profits are divided half to each class of shares.

Details of the Nantlle Vale company, as listed in Skinner's *Mining Manual and Yearbook*, 1926.

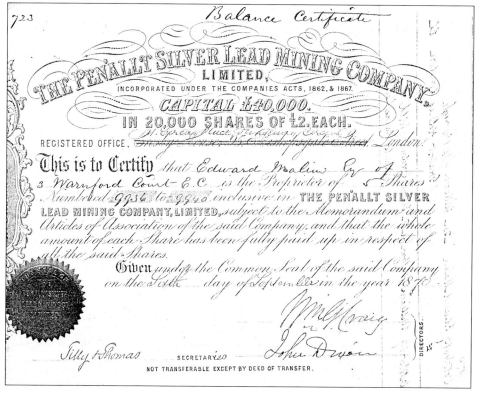

A Pen'Allt share certificate of 1870.

Close to the main road between Nantlle and Talysarn is **GWERNOR** (502525), a forgotten copper mine dating at least from 1755, and bearing witness to considerable workings, of which something can be glimpsed from a report of a legal action to recover wages due.[38]

According to the evidence the company included Thomas Turner Molineaux, his father and sister Priscilla, Messers Meyrick, Buckingham and Leigh the cashier. In August 1843 Benjamin Tucker the agent set a bargain with six men. £2 per ton was to be paid for ore raised, 10 shillings per month being deduced for use of the engine (waterwheel). The shaft was at least 16 fathoms deep and in the autumn of 1843 between 22 and 41 tons of ore were raised – the evidence is conflicting – and sold at Amlwch. We may suppose the total output exceeded these figures, and in addition some 32 tons were returned in 1867.

In 1982 I wrote of the site:

'The lode strikes up a steep hillside by a wood behind Gwernor farmhouse and has been worked by three shafts close together. These are fenced by a fine assortment of old railway lines including bridge, J section and fish-belly, which may in part have derived from an adjacent slate quarry, reputedly the oldest in the valley. The lowest shaft housed the pumps and nearby is a wheelpit of massive construction, about 36ft x 4½ ft within.

The dumps are largely grassgrown but reveal very iron-stained and gossany material. On one side of the apparent entrance to a shallow adit is a vertical rock-face, probably a wall of

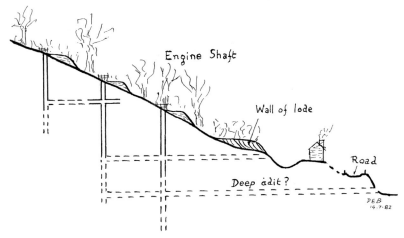

A section of Gwernor, as deduced from surface evidence in 1981.

the lode, and there are signs of a deep adit driven beneath the road. Water still flows along the mine leat, and at one time powered a small waterwheel for domestic purposes at the farmhouse, where a stone aqueduct and diminutive wheelpit still remain'.

Since then, Gwernor has been transformed by a landscape gardener.

Beyond the eastern end of the Nantlle valley near the village of Rhyd-ddu, the 1st edition 6" Ordnance map marks *Old Shaft (Copper)*, close to the Welsh Highland narrow-gauge railway. This was **FFRIDD ISAF** (574534) a mine of little account, but worth a passing reference.

In 1851 it was said to be a recent discovery, and something of its history can be assembled from three reports, the more intelligible of which is probably attributable to Matthew Francis.[39] The first, by G. Davey, 20th August 1853, refers to old workings 'beginning at the road all the way (so far as opened out) for about ¹/₂ mile in length to the Eastern Mine'. Seven years later, John Jones of Beddgelert recorded three parallel east-west lodes and a north-south lode in the western part of the sett where a level had been driven and yielding 'many a ton' of ore. The third report, undated, states 'the deepest workings are about 300 yards east of the road where there is a shaft sunk about 20 yards and several Tons of good Copper ores raised producing about 20 per cent'. To the east were washing floors and a blacksmith's shop, also a cross-cut from the brook driven 17 yards west on a lode, showing a little copper.

A lease dated 13 November 1863 identified John Griffith of Portmadoc as the landlord, and James Hamer of Reddish Green, Stockport as tenant of part of Ffriddisaf farm, with powers to mine for lead and copper and 'to make railways or wagon or other roads on the land leased'.[40]

The main workings, just below the Welsh Highland Railway, consisted of two narrow opencuts about 20ft deep on an east-west lode, and joined by a short level, the whole extending 40 or 50 yards altogether. The eastern end had been accessible by a cutting driven in from lower ground near a waste-tip, but now much overgrown. Whether any work has been done after the 1860s seems unlikely.

Some of the workings in the Beddgelert area are very ancient, perhaps even Bronze Age. Many either re-opened or started for the first time in the late 17th century when copper fetched a high price. According to Gruffydd Pritchard, a miner writing in 1860, they included Brynfelin, Aberglaslyn, Sygun, Crib Ddu (Llwyndu) and Lliwedd. He also recorded prospecting for lead in Gwasted Annas, Bwlch Mwlchan and Lliwedd Bach 'but a hundred times more waste than substance was got in them all'.[1a] Pritchard went on to castigate bad management and high overheads for ruining the chances of many workings, and his observations were no doubt largely justified.

In the vicinity of Aberglaslyn Pass, a beautiful area that abounds with tourists, mines of copper have been extensively wrought, the nearest to Beddgelert being **BRYNFELIN** (589472). It was for long a part of the Beddgelert Estate which included Sygun, and owned by the Jones' of Bryntirion near Bangor. According to a local author, Brynfelin was worked well before the middle of the sixteenth century [1b], and about 1746 Alexander Fraser, a miner and Elizabeth his wife lived at the nearby Bryn y Felin house. Fraser was an enigmatic character, reputedly a murderer, who later took part in discovering the vast deposits of copper ore at Parys Mountain in Anglesey.[1c]

The mine was drained by a long adit emerging as deep as possible near the banks of the River Glaslyn, and reminiscent of the levels driven regardless of expense by the 17th century entrepreneur Thomas Bushell at the silver mines of Cardiganshire.[2] It no doubt originated prior to the 1760s when Brynfelin was said to be doing well, with a dressing plant and stamps, and twenty men underground.[3]

Those were the best days, for the 19th century witnessed a succession of re-openings and every one a failure. In 1802 the mine belonged to Thomas Jones of Bryntirion and although working 'with great spirit and prospect of success',[4] within a few years he advertised a mill for letting which had been used for crushing 'mineral stone' from the mine no longer active. A suggested adaptation to a woollen factory implied a substantial building, and on the premises was an almost new waterwheel made in Liverpool.[5]

Whether or not this improbable transformation ever materialised, ore was again sold in the 1830s, and in 1838 the Brynfelin company wanted to acquire Sygun but the proposition came to nothing. After a period of closure the mine was going once more in a small way in 1851.[6]

With the intention of extending the operations of a private venture, the Brynfelin Copper Mining Company Ltd. formed in April 1861 with a nominal capital of £6,000.[7] The promoters included William Hawes of Manchester; John Evans, mine and quarry

A general view of Brynfelin. The lodes and open-workings run from left to right just behind the dumps. *David Bick*

This powder magazine without its conical roof stands on a rocky knoll at Brynfelin. The inside is only 6ft across, and once had a wooden floor to avoid sparks from the miners' boots. *David Bick*

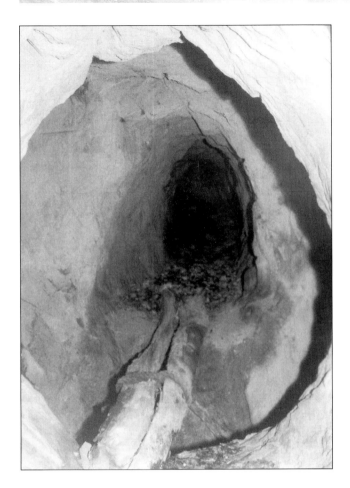

A crude timber bridge straddles an open winze at Brynfelin.
John Burman

agent of Penmorfa; Thomas Fuller, mining agent, Edgar Yarrow and Horatio Nelson. There were said to be three veins a few feet apart, the main lode had yielded 7 tons of ore per cubic fathom, and 515 tons had been sold for £3,736. The adit was said to be driving east towards a junction of lodes, and Captain Matthew Francis reported upon the prospects. By July 1861 the engine shaft had been sunk 5 fathoms under adit, but before the close of the year there arose 'insuperable difficulties to the company carrying out the intention expressed', of which lack of ore was no doubt the greatest. Following an application for a dissolution, the venture vanished into obscurity.[8]

The *Carnarvon & Denbigh Herald* advertised Brynfelin for sale in July and December 1864, and four years later 16 tons of ore were returned, perhaps from picking over the dumps. In July 1875 the mine again came on the market, on this occasion being offered by the executors of James Hamer. It included a newly erected machine house, dressing-house, turbine wheel and machinery, all in good working order. The sett amounted to 35 acres with a royalty of 1/16th, but it is doubtful whether any development followed.[9]

Many features of Brynfelin can still be traced. The stamps building probably stood between the main road and river. A leat brought water for the wheel a few hundred yards, tapping the river near the bridge of the Welsh Highland Railway that came too late to help the mines. The tree-lined watercourse cut out of solid rock for much of the way is worth exploring.

A long trench leads to the run-in adit portal and points to the mine, where on a rocky knoll in a nearby wood stands a roofless powder magazine. To the south-west of it is a ruined dwelling and dumps with a dangerous shaft and a horse-whim circle with an iron pedestal-bearing at its centre. Long and deep opencuts reveal two nearly parallel lodes striking up a gloomy wooded hillside, a silent and mysterious setting which puts us strongly in mind of prehistoric iron mines or Scowles in the Forest of Dean, and perhaps in point of time, their origins were not so very far removed.

Towards Porthmadog in the precipitous western slopes of the Aberglaslyn Pass, the Old Series one-inch Geological map shows two lodes about 400ft apart, striking south south-west.

The first of these was worked at **LEVEL GOCH** or Red Level (593466), an adit marked on Ordnance maps as 'Chalybeate Spring'. On the rocky hillside high above are also shown 'Old Shafts', and in this area are said to exist several deep gashes where ore has been removed. In 1907 the works were beyond living memory, and at that period according to tradition, the adit had been driven to the limit of ventilation provided by a water-powered fan of some sort at the level's mouth. [10] How far the level extended can only be conjectured, but surface trials extend a great distance along the strike of the vein.

Only a bubbling spring of ochreous water emerging from a small square hole in a wall alongside the road now identifies the mouth of Level Goch. The wall stands right across the entrance, and if the former is contemporary with the road, which was built in the early 1800s, we may assume the level has been abandoned for two centuries.

Quite probably, Level Goch worked in conjunction with **ABERGLASLYN** (594462) where copper is supposed to have been known to the Romans. Something of Aberglaslyn's history is preserved in correspondence between John Griffiths and Lord Powys, who as we have seen, dabbled in Caernarvonshire mines in hopes of recouping his losses elsewhere. In January 1769, less than a year after the great discovery of copper at Parys Mountain, Griffiths wrote enthusiastically 'I saw a Vein of Copper in young Sir Watkins Estate by Pontaberglaslyn which is open to the Day about a yard wide; and as soon as Sir Watkin is of Age I am told that great application will be made for a Lease . . . I think I may venture to say that your Lordship can never do a more promising Act for Profit in the mining way possible . . .'. Later, he again pressed his opinions. 'Your Lordship will find there the noblest Vein with such prospect for Profit I ever saw'.

Eighteen months afterwards, Griffiths informed him 'I've had an account that Pontaberglaslyn copper vein is now worked by Sir Watkin Williams himself and that they get good copper in it, and that it promises to turn out well'. What Powys rejoindered is not recorded. Griffiths also added that Chauncey Townsend, the Cardiganshire mine promoter and copper smelter of Swansea, had the promise of a lease of the works. [11]

An 18th century print of a shaft in the Aberglaslyn Pass. Note the hand windlass and the donkeys laden with panniers for carrying ore.

It is worth recalling that at this time, although no proper road existed through the pass, Aberglaslyn (mouth of the Glaslyn river) boasted a sea-port with wharf and anchorage from which ore could conveniently be shipped. Subsequent to construction of the barrage at Porthmadog the sea retreated six miles and the village fell largely into decay.

During his tours in 1810, Richard Fenton observed opposite Pont Aberglaslyn 'an adit of a copper mine now working by some Cornish Adventurers who are laying out a great deal of money, as if there was a great prospect of advantage'. A year or two afterwards, a stamping mill was reported on the site, the landowner being a Mr. Lloyd. [12]

According to Samuel Lewis nearly 30 years later, 'near Pont Aber Glaslyn, copper ore has been found in great abundance but the copper was so intermixed with other ores as to render it very difficult of separation with any advantage to the proprietors. About the year 1800 the high price of copper induced some adventurers to renew the works from which great quantities of ore were obtained for some years; but they were again discontinued and remained in a neglected state till 1819, since when

These stopes on the Aberglaslyn lode show a witness of the floor of the original level as a ledge on the right hand side. Quite often, levels have a timber floor to bridge extensive stoping beneath, and thus are liable to collapse.
David Bick

many hundred tons have been procured annually'.

From 1804 to 1847 only 56 tons (in 1838/9) were sold at Swansea. Since these are the sole official statistics, this example will serve to illustrate the deficiency of this source over the period concerned.

From the report of a mining engineer recorded in 1907, nothing had been done at Aberglaslyn since the mid-nineteenth century when it came into the possession of J.W. Greaves. He is said to have closed the mine which was giving employment to about 25 men working on tribute, and demolished a roller-crushing mill. The report made out a good case for re-opening the working which had been 'carried on in a most primitive manner indicating a hand-to-mouth policy', but it does not appear that any developments followed.

A deep adit emerged immediately behind Bridge House, which must have been built after the mine closed. When I explored the workings in 1955 it served the purpose of a larder, and after about 50 yards reached the lode, thence a short distance to a fall. Higher up, a series of adits, shafts and deep and extensive opencuts, no doubt descending to adit, occupied part of the garden. Higher still, the ground levelled out and there were further workings, with a waterwheel pit, perhaps for driving the stamps prior to the roller-crushing mill near Pont yr Afon Goch. These lodes of the Aberglaslyn Pass are nowadays very difficult to explore for one reason or another, but there can be little doubt they yielded plenty in their time.

In rugged country to the north-east, ancient and extensive trials for copper extend to the Vale of Gwynant. At least one of the lodes correlates with the Aberglaslyn workings, and in places the area seems hardly less than a stockwork.

In the vicinity of Cwmbuchan the mines were known as **NANTMOR** or **CWMBUCHAN** (602472). The exact boundaries are uncertain and whether these titles signified different workings has not been possible to decide. The first mining here is reported to date from 1720.[13]

These workings on the lode outcrop at Nantmor descend to the adit level. *C J Williams*

The copper works of Cwmbuchan were in their heydey between 1782 and 1802, and in 1811 a Mr. Tregoning living in Aberglaslyn was a supervisor for Sygun and Nantmor. In later years the fame of the Nantmor miners led to their being asked to drive tunnels for the Oakley quarries, some of which were named after them.[14]

The Cwm Buchan Silver Lead Mining Co. was registered in 1870 to operate the Nantmor mine, but work done on a north lode had ceased by 1875. Half a century afterwards, the Nantmor Copper Co. Ltd. was formed with £9,070 issued capital, and financed by the Welsh Copper Trust Ltd. The main activity consisted of a good show at surface including an aerial ropeway nearly a mile long supplied by R. White & Sons, Widnes, leading to a concentration plant near the Welsh Highland Railway.[15a] Little, if any, ore actually passed through the mill, and four years later the venture descended into voluntary liquidation. According to Dawson Ware, the levels at Nantmor intersected a rich pocket of arsenical copper-sulphide (copper-pyrites?) with concentrates assaying 1-3 dwt of gold per ton. There were also workings on a north lode showing galena.

The industrial archaeology of Cwm Buchan is impressive. As at Gilfach the geography has spared it, and we cannot avoid the impression of a great deal of money sunk and lost. A short walk from the carpark at Nantmor leads through a bridge under the Welsh Highland Railway to the lower end of the ropeway and the mill. The extensive remains are not easily interpreted. They include walls, concrete tanks, platforms and two large buddle circles for treating the finely crushed ore. A prominent sight is a tall iron cage 8ft high and 4ft diameter with a pulley above standing close to foundations which were no doubt part of the ropeway; it was loaded with rocks to maintain a tension in the cable. Higher up the valley a long line of steel towers still survive, the terminus with its large wheel for the cable being still in good condition and close to two adits.

The lower end of the ropeway in Cwm Buchan. The iron cage held rocks to tension the cable, and the two heavy vertical iron spindles were no doubt part of the mechanism. The purpose of the concrete platforms is uncertain.   *David Bick*

The round buddle in the foreground is a prominent feature at the mill site. Behind, the bridge under the Welsh Highland Railway leads to a carpark and the A 4085 road at Nantmor.   *David Bick*

Damian McCurdy examines the terminus at the beginning of the aerial ropeway in Cwm Buchan. It is still complete and in good condition.　　　*C J Williams*

The lower level is a crosscut and the lode reveals a strong quartz vein with copper-staining. It is stoped out to daylight 100 ft above, the period of working being uncertain. A row of surface trials reveal the strike of the lode, and beyond trial levels dot the mountain nearly all the way to **SYGUN** (606486).[15b]

According to a prospectus issued in 1836, Sygun had been worked by adits during the past six or seven years, and ores sold to a value exceeding £2,800.[16] The deepest workings were only about 20 fathoms below the summit of the hill, but a level had been driven in a little lower, to provide drainage. This level was about 66 fathoms above the valley floor, but had not been completed.

Matthew Francis, then chief agent to John Taylor & Sons, Lisburne Mines, near Aberystwyth, submitted a favourable report. The level could be finished for only about £50, and £350 was estimated for a crushing mill, to be supplied by water from Llyn Dinas. The promoters also secured grants from Sir Richard Bulkeley Williams of land to the north and east, 'on the range of the veins worked by the levels before described'. This area was known as **LLWYNDU** or **CRIB DDU** (606483), both with alternative spellings, and figured prominently in the developments.[17]

The solicitors in the concern were Jones & Jeffries, Carmarthen, the treasurers being Jones, Williams & Co., Llanelly. The board included R.W. Jones, John Budd of Liverpool, John Jeffries, William Williams, Morgan Williams of Llanelly, William Bevan, John Tregellas, Nevill Broom and Robert Dunkin of Loughor Colliery, who was later described as pompous.[18] Most of these men were also involved in the Llechfraith Mine near Dolgellau and Moelwyn slate quarry, ailing ventures managed

Sygun Mine Company.

Capital—£3,000,

IN 600 SHARES OF £5 EACH.

—◦|◦|◦|◦—

Deposit—£2 PER SHARE,

Provisional Committee.

JOHN BUDD, Esq.	NEVILL BROOM, Esq.
R. W. JONES, Esq.	JOHN T. TREGELLAS, Esq.
JOHN B. JEFFRIES, Esq.	WILLIAM BEVAN, Esq.
ROBERT DUNKIN, Esq.	EVAN JAMES, Esq
WILLIAM WILLIAMS, Esq.	THOMAS BEVAN, Esq.
MORGAN WILLIAMS, Esq.	

Treasurers.

MESSRS. JONES, WILLIAMS, & Co., BANKER's, LLANELLY.

Solicitors.

MESSRS. JONES, & JEFFRIES, CARMARTHEN.

Mineral Surveyor.

MATTHEW FRANCIS, Esq.

A detail from the Prospectus of the Sygun Mine Company, 1836. *NLW*

by Robert Byers.[19] The Moelwyn quarry was not the one usually so called, but on the opposite side of the mountain from Ffestiniog at a place known as Pantmawr.[20]

In the beginning the expectations for Sygun were boundless, and the company resolved to send two of the committee to Beddgelert to complete the transaction. 'Now my dear sir' wrote Dunkin to Jeffries, 'what do you say to a trip to one of the most beautiful parts of North Wales – all your expenses will of course be paid … you must lay aside all other business to go'. He proposed to catch the night mail from Carmarthen to Hereford on the Friday, then the Liverpool mail to Shrewsbury and thence by the Holyhead mail to Bangor, 'where we should reach by Tuesday evening'. But there was still some 25 miles to cover, and so a journey which nowadays would take a few hours by a much shorter route needed the best part of a week, not to mention the cost and discomfort. The difficulties of transport in those days, and the problems of management at a distance when the fastest message was the speed of a horse, are all too readily forgotten.

One early development was the construction of a leat from Llyn Dinas to feed a crushing mill alongside the river. But ore sales were slow and the lessor, David White Griffith, was involved in doubtful dealings with the mine captain, Robert Roberts, and their connivance was to bring the company much anxiety and distress. Griffith soon became restless at the lack of progress, and perhaps with reason, since as we shall see shortly, a valuable discovery had been made just over the hill at Llwyndu, and was taking much attention. He therefore brought an action seeking ejectment for breach of contract, claiming that his mines had been 'most improperly and injudiciously worked'. In fact, the management wanted to abandon Sygun altogether and form a new company, but trouble with shareholders delayed the proposal.

By the summer of 1839 the Llechfraith and Moelwyn ventures verged on collapse, though James Spooner, engineer to the Ffestiniog Railway opened in 1836, was

An attempt to sell a quarter share in Llwyndu in June 1841. *NLW*

VALUABLE
COPPER MINE,

Beddgelert, North Wales.

𝔚𝔥𝔦𝔠𝔥 𝔴𝔦𝔩𝔩 𝔟𝔢 𝔖𝔬𝔩𝔡 𝔟𝔶 𝔄𝔲𝔠𝔱𝔦𝔬𝔫, 𝔟𝔶

MR. C. WARTON,

At the Auction Mart, opposite the Bank of England,

ON WEDNESDAY, 16TH JUNE, 1841,

AT TWELVE o'CLOCK, IN ONE LOT.

𝔓𝔞𝔯𝔱𝔦𝔠𝔲𝔩𝔞𝔯𝔰 & 𝔠𝔬𝔫𝔡𝔦𝔱𝔦𝔬𝔫𝔰 of 𝔖𝔞𝔩𝔢,

OF

ONE FOURTH PART, OR SHARE

OF AND IN THE

LLWYNDU, OR BLACK BUSH MINE.

A general view of Llwyndu showing the original workings near the top, with the adit emerging onto the dressing floors in the foreground. The whim shaft is behind the high ground to the right.

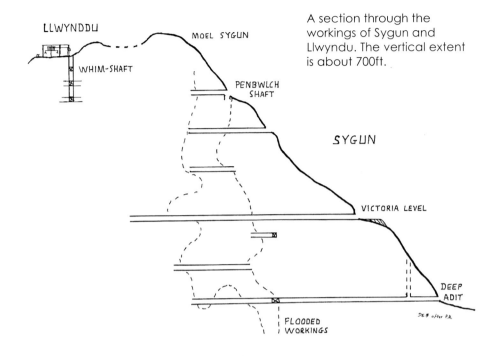

LLWYNDDU

MOEL SYGUN

A section through the workings of Sygun and Llwyndu. The vertical extent is about 700ft.

WHIM-SHAFT

PENBWLCH SHAFT

SYGUN

VICTORIA LEVEL

DEEP ADIT

DEB after P.R.

FLOODED WORKINGS

requested to make a survey of the quarry at a sum not exceeding £25. At the same time the Sygun company changed its name to the Llwyndu Mine Company and the board now included Robert Byers, who was also acting as manager.

The Sygun Fawr and Hafodydd Brithion estates were offered for sale in September 1839, having 'a beautiful River and Lakes abounding with salmon and Trout, amidst some of the most sublime and romantic scenery in North Wales... The Copper Mine ... is now in hand with powerful waterwork and other machinery'.[21] The advertisement also announced that 'it is expected that a rail-road will be shortly formed to the shipping place [Porthmadog] by the owners of adjoining mines' – a much desired improvement often attempted but never achieved.

Dunkin left the Llwyndu board in 1840, but in spite of the promising start prospects went from bad to worse. In April 1842 the Monmouthshire and Glamorganshire Bank refused to extend the overdraft, whereupon Byers turned to the North & South Wales bank. This ended in a lawsuit involving the latter v Byers and partners as defendants. Llwyndu came up for sale in April 1845, but he was still on the scene in 1847, the company then being in the hands of trustees. The venture finally subsided beneath a mass of debt and litigation.

Turning now to the mine itself, although a little ore had been returned from the sett in earlier years, Llwyndu was apparently a virgin find, as can be gathered from Byers' letter to Dunkin, dated 25 July 1838.

A section of the Llwyndu workings by Robert Byers. A, Crosscut adit; B, Ore, 9-10 inches wide; C, Lode, 3-4ft wide of mundic; D, Sinking to meet E, splendid lode here, 29% copper.

NLW

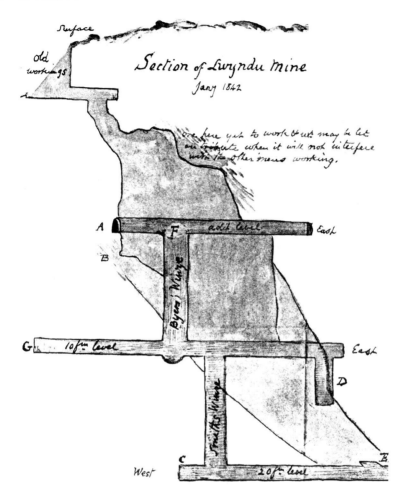

I have just returned from Amlwch where I have been with five samples of the new ore. The result of one of them is *15 per Cent!!* I could have had a higher produce had I taken single pieces of the vein or metal, but I had about 3 cwt taken down from the mountain & crushed & from *that* took my samples this vein of Grey ore with native copper Green & blue Carbonate in it, is 500 yards from our other works and about 1000 ft from the bottom of the mountain.

The difficulties with Griffith were however, giving cause for concern. 'I much fear him' continued Byers, 'we have been over the mines and to Byers lode or Sygun New Mines, and I told him I would do everything in my power to put the mine in order'. Nevertheless, although several hundred tons of ore were sold, the company ceased work at Sygun as we have seen.

Pascoe's sketch of the new shaft, horsewhim and dressing arrangements. The walled whim-circle has a stone pedestal bearing in the centre.   *NLW, John Burman*

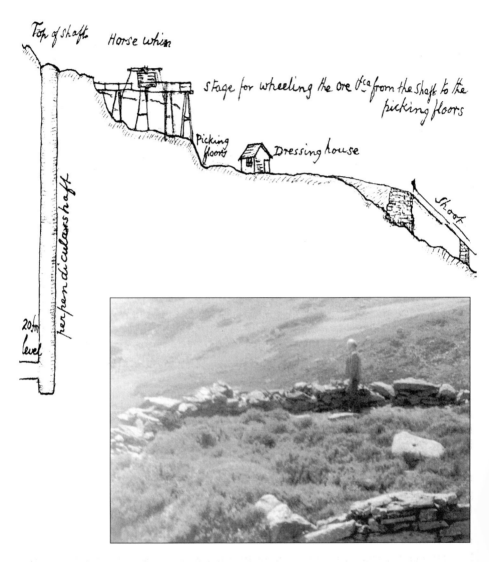

Captain William Pascoe became agent, and in September 1839 Byers' winze was sinking below adit at Llwyndu. 50 or 60 tons of ore were ready for market at $8^{1}/_{2}\%$ copper, and some specimens assayed as high as 30%. The dressing was done by twenty girls, 'the cheapest thing we have on the mine and without them it is hardly possible to know what we should do'. Byers now planned a road down to the turnpike, and was building a timber shed for an office and room for the girls to dry their clothes, 'to keep them as comfortable and happy as possible for I assure you they are quite essential to our success'.

By the end of 1841, workings were down to the 20 fathom level, with a horse-whim and vertical shaft to the east which communicated with the level by a cross-cut. The shaft enabled water and ore to be raised, gave better access and ventilation, and assisted the objective of removing the dressing operations lower down the hill, it being 'impossible for men or horses to stand the weather'. Floods were also interfering with ore waggons fording Llyn Dinas, but of greater disquiet was the general deterioration in the lode, both laterally and in depth.

In the summer of 1842 the company resolved at a general meeting to dispose of the mine and materials by auction or private contract – a decision which Pascoe did his best to persuade Byers to reverse.

'Now Sir, you must be well aware with myself that the mine is only just now brought into a state of proper working having made a communication with our Perpendicular Shaft . We have also made every thing convenient to the shaft at surface for discharging the stuff, in our Dressing department, such as new ore Floors, necessary Dressing Houses, erecting wood shoots for conveying the ore down the Mountain, which has also considerably reduced the price of carriage to the Shipping places – These different conveniences, together with the Shaft, cost the Company about £1500 – This Sum, they should have had in their pockets if they had only told me they did not want to make a Mine of it...'

This appeal may have had an effect, for the company continued for several years. But good facilities and conveniences on surface provided no compensation for lack of ore. Luck was against the adventurers, although according to Robert Hunt this rich bunch returned 685 tons of copper ore at Swansea from 1840 to 1842. Some ore of course may have gone elsewhere.

Since that time little or nothing has been done, but when we visit the site complete with Byer's letters and Pascoe's plans, taking the road made from Llyn Dinas, the old scene revives before us. There, under the highest point of the mountain are stopes descending from the original discovery, and the adit emerging at an area paved with flat stones where the ore was crushed and separated from the waste rock. Large heaps broken down by the girls remain as their memorial, and the shells of several buildings testify to the passage of time.

Over a ridge is the vertical shaft and horsewhim circle with a bucking house near the road below. In the vicinity a great deal of material not much bigger than road-gravel is difficult to account for, also a stone flue perhaps for calcining the ore, features to which the documentary records probably hold the key.

Returning now to Sygun, we find that at some time after its abandonment following the breach of contract episode, Charles Wing of Grove End, Middlesex, and Henry Stock of Plas Gwynant took up the mine together with Hafod-y-llan and Bryn Mostyn slate quarry.[22] In April 1841 Stock withdrew, and in the same month Henry McKellar of Wandsworth Lodge, Surrey became involved in the mines, with Alan Searell a native of Devon acting as general manager.[23] The connection between Wing and McKellar is obscure, but the latter maintained a strong interest until his death twenty-one years later. The concern appears to have operated as the Sygun & Hafodyllain Mining Company.

Searell's work included opening a slate quarry later known as South Snowdon, and in the autumn of 1841 he was sinking Pen Bwlch Shaft and driving on the lode at

Sygun. Tributors worked the mine, and from a report in 1843 something is gathered of the underground developments.

17 men are working in a rise in the bottom level in the winze in No.3 sinking and stopeing and dressing the copper. In the rise they are working in the lode which is about 2ft wide, in about nine inches of it there is a good mixture of ore. They are also sinking the winze made by Messrs Byers & Co. to facilitate the communication which will effectually drain and ventilate the mine.

Over 27 tons of ore had been raised and dressed in the past three months, and from May to December, 82 tons were shipped to Liverpool by coaster. By the end of 1843, trials at the slate quarry had turned out well. Searell was now pressing McKellar for the full annual salary of £150 which had been agreed two years before, and there was also another bone of contention.

If you wish me to stop in this house through the winter something must be done as the wind and rain come through the walls in such a manner that it is almost impossible to remain in it, besides it is much too small for my family, if about £36 were laid out in building another room and cementing the walls it might answer for the present...

Shortly afterwards, Searell gave in his notice. Cwmorthin quarry near Blaenau Ffestiniog was just opening, and he gained a position there at £200 per year 'besides a comfortable house, garden and with ground to keep a horse and cows which will

Sygun Copper Mine, soon after re-opening for tourists. The shell of the Elmore flotation plant climbs the hill in the background.

make a great difference in my family in comparison with what I have hitherto been in receipt of '.

The parting must have been amicable, for Searell's brother Philip, who had assisted in making plans for a railway, was hoping for the post. Searell himself expressed a willingness to render whatever service he could, Cwmorthin being as he put it, 'not much over two hours walk from the Snowdon quarries'. He left unsaid that the round trip amounted to 12 or 13 miles, most of it merely sheep tracks over the roof of Wales, for journeys such as this were nothing out of the ordinary on top of a day's work.

Whether McKellar regretted his treatment of Searell is not recorded, but at all events the relationship had reverted to the old footing by 1856. As to developments in the intervening years little is known, although the thread can be followed after Searell's return. Tributors were still engaged at Sygun, where in the meanwhile a crosscut adit had been driven from the bottom of the mountain. The crusher put up by Byers & partners had done much work, for the brass bearings under the rollers were described as quite worn out.

On 19th October 1858 Searell wrote to McKellar regarding the underground state of affairs, and added 'I hope you will yet get satisfactory information respecting Capt. W.V. Williams and his party for I do not feel justified in recommending you to pay out more money at Sygun after hearing so much from Mr. Pathereck whose opinion stands *second* to none in mineing matters.[24] At the same time I do hope Sygun will turn out better than Mr. P. contemplates'.

McKellar had been trying to dispose of his unprofitable interests even as early as 1843, but without success.

...n the adit level at Sygun. Note the fragile iron-oxide stalagtites and the deposits of ...ochre.

A schedule of materials at Sygun at the end of 1858 confirms that the works then centred around the deep adit, and gives a good idea of the primitive equipment typical of 19th century metal mines. The following items were included:

Office 2 writing desks, 2 cupboards, 2 stools, iron fire fender.

Store 5 waggon wheels, harness 3 Double, 3 Single, 3 Spalling, 5 Cobbing hammers, 4 Buckers, 2 picks, crowbar, 5 100lb drills, 3 hand sieves, 3 wheel-barrows, 16 shovels, 4 picking boxes, 95 yds rope, 5 cogwheels, iron sheet 5ft x 2ft, 221b fencing wire, iron bearing for crushers, 2 cast wheels for gigers [jiggers] 57ft iron pumps, 7 new sieve bottoms.

Adit level 64 yds loose rails, 220 yds of Rail Road, viz, 176 yds to mouth of level and 44 yds outside. One iron waggon, one wood waggon, 6 cobbing irons, waterwheel l4ft x 2ft and drum complete.

Smithy 7 pairs of tongs, sledge, 3 small hammers, 561b of punches, chisels, setts and mandrels. 4 screw cutting plates, tool box, anvil and vice, bellows, 2 cwt scrap.

Carpenters Shop Carpenters bench, chopping stock.

Lower [Dressing] Floor Iron water wheel 13ft x 4ft 6in with rollers and 8 stamp heads, one pair spare rollers, small gigging water wheel and apparatus with 2 hutches. Two sieves 4ft x 2ft, shed over engine and crushers, beam scales and weights. One triangle, picking table and tub.

Useless Old boat, old zinc pipe, slate cutting model and part of a pumping machine.

Sygun struggled on, and in 1862 Captain Julian of Simdde Dylluan examined the workings. Little was now in progress, and the death of McKellar shortly afterwards brought a long and disappointing chapter to an end.

The mine returned 78 tons of ore in 1868-70, and was taken over in 1882 or 3 by Henry Maudslay of Westminster Palace Hotel, London, and his agent Charles Kneebone of Betws-y-Coed.[25] Both men had interests in mines near Llanrwst, and for a few years kept several employed at Sygun.

Kneebone claimed at least fourteen well-defined copper lodes existed in Sygun and Crib Ddu, and referred in one part of the latter to a lode 7ft thick running 50% sulphur (iron-pyrites) and $3^1/_2$-5% copper. Five adits had been driven from the west totalling 400 fathoms, with levels connected and ready for stoping. Kneebone also mentioned a large lode of iron ore, a true caunter lode, 6-10ft wide and the same as on the Perthi Estate to the west, where it had yielded manganese ores of some value. Sygun, he considered, was attributable to the Romans, though later operations had destroyed virtually all the evidence.

Maudslay eventually dropped out but Kneebone, we may suspect to attract another victim, corresponded in July 1896 with Alexander Stanley Elmore of Roundhay, Leeds, and made claims to certain grades of ore.[27]

The mine was now about to enter its final, most technically advanced, most costly, and most commercially disastrous phase, and towards a better understanding of the period a few words of explanation are necessary.

In the same year, 1896, Elmore's father had acquired a large stake in the Glasdir copper mine near Dolgellau, a low-grade deposit which conventional ore-dressing machinery could not work at a profit. As a consequence, the epoch-making principle of flotation as a means of separating sulphide ores was here conceived, and Stanley Elmore described how it came about.[28]

My brother and I were asked to investigate and see if the extraction could be improved. On one of our visits it was observed that at the angle where one of the launders carrying the waterborne pulp deflected the stream, some splashing took place, and it so happened also that oil had dripped onto the outside of the launder at this point from a shaft-bearing immediately overhead; a strong sun was shining upon it and a glittering reflection attracted the eye.

On examination it was noted that adhering to the oil was a coating of what appeared to be quite clean copper-pyrite and it was remarked that no rock seemed to adhere to the oily surface. A little later a piece of ordinary 2-inch iron steam-pipe, which was in such a position that the discharge from one of the slime-launders splashed against it; was found by to have a clear picture of a man's hand printed on it in bright copper-pyrite. It had been carried in a greasy hand, and the whole of that part of the surface which had received a very thin coating of grease by contact with the hand subsequently became coated with pyrite. It was these two accidental observations which led to the invention of the flotation process.

Frank Elmore took out a patent in 1898, and the new method of mineral separation first proved itself a practical proposition in Glasdir.[29a] We have it on the authority of Walter McDermott, a collaborator and close friend of Stanley Elmore, that the next two mines to apply the process – with little or no publicity – were Sygun and Clogau St. Davids near Bontddu. Thus was born and bred in Wales a technique of incalculable value, and one for which the Elmores received due credit, providing at least a consolation for the patent infringements and litigation that haunted the family for years afterwards.

The Elmores and others strove constantly to improve the process which even today is still developing, and it is regrettable that so little of the initial work has come to light, except as broad-brush recollections. But at the time of a great discovery, spirits are carried aloft at the prospect and souls are too pre-occupied with practical difficulties and matters scarcely understood to bear in mind posterity. Machines are modified, rebuilt and scrapped in rapid succession, and obsolete drawings and correspondence summarily cast aside. In the end, nothing of early prototypes or day-to-day developments endures, except by chance, to recall the pioneers and the path of progress that they followed.

Stanley Elmore lived till 1944, and papers may yet survive, though attempts to trace them have met with no success. Still, it must be hoped that the full story of these historic trials in the mountains of Wales will one day be told.[29b]

After this interlude we return to the year 1897, when Stanley Elmore was listed as owner of Sygun, with Kneebone as agent, and a few men employed underground. To exploit the patents, the British Ore Concentration Syndicate became incorporated in December 1900. Its offices were at St. Helens Place, London, the directors being A.H. Rowe, H.W. Blundell and Lord Teynham, who already held a seat on the board of several South African gold mining companies.[30] Sygun and Cribddu were the main object of attention with options also held on Arran (Hafod-y-porth). In 1902, several additional directors were appointed including Stanley Elmore, and a year later his brother Frank became consultant metallurgist.

With regard to the deposit to be worked J.H. Collins F.G.S., past President of the Institute of Mining, reported. His lowest estimate of the ore available came to 480,000 tons, and he reckoned that a scale of 200 tons per day would yield £37,000 annual

Young adventurers
outside the
Victoria Level at
Sygun before it
was developed as
part of the tourist
attraction.
David Bick

profit. Collins concluded by claiming the estimates conservative in the highest degree, and in particular that much more ore would be available than mentioned.[31]

In the event, a 100 ton throughput mill was erected, including a 20 stamp battery, four Wilfley tables and four Elmore concentrator units manufactured by Frazer and Chalmers. A steam engine and two Crossley gas engines of 200 hp provided the power.[32]

The mill was located on a rocky knoll cut out in a series of steps, with a road alongside for traction engines, ore being trammed in at the top via a timber bridge over a ravine. The tramway led by a long curving embankment from the Victoria tunnel, a cross-cut level commencing above the old deep adit. 100 yards inside, a rise communicated 125 ft to No.3 level. No.4 was 90 ft below surface and 60 ft above No.3, giving 275 ft of backs above the Victoria tunnel. This underground development largely existed when the company took over, and work was also done to the north-east at Cae Moch. The manager was Edward Skewes.[33]

The mill and other activities proved very costly, and by the A.G.M. of 1902 finances were nearly exhausted. There was talk of raising another £50,000 ostensibly to develop other options. The chairman, Lord Teynham, made much of the low cost of mining, and as for the mill 'everything is working so smoothly and automatically that it reminded me of the machines in Chicago where the pig goes in one end and the sausage comes out of the other . . . everything is working well, but at the same time it is too early yet to speak of results'.[31]

In reality it was not too early at all, except for Teynsham's reluctance to utter the truth. The venture was proving incapable of meeting expenses, far less paying dividend, and it is doubtful if profit could have been achieved even excluding the costs of dressing. 20 men were working underground in 1903, and that first and final year of sales produced 410 tons of concentrates worth only £923, a derisory amount in view of the forecast. Technically the Elmore process had worked but commercially, due to an ore running less than 1% and hopeless copper prices, it proved a disaster.

In addition, Stanley Elmore in May 1904 lost a lawsuit with costs after Charles Kneebone sued him for £932 – a large figure in days when working men earned £30 a year. The sum amounted to interest due upon £3,750 of debentures which Elmore had agreed to issue to him, but from 1902 he had withheld further payments when the mine proved a failure. Kneebone had already received £1,250 for procurring the lease, and Elmore stated that the former in his letter of July 1896 had fraudulently quoted ore values that existed only in hand-picked specimens. In response, the plaintiff asserted that Elmore had himself analysed samples before deciding to proceed.[27]

In the beginning, with little or no experience of mining, Elmore was as yet at the mercy of promoters, and probably in the flush of enthusiasm had indeed not fully established the grade. But from the report of the case in conjunction with other evidence, we cannot escape the feeling that the verdict was severe. Reading between the lines of the judge's remarks, Elmore could have won had he taken the initiative and brought a fraud charge at an early stage. But Kneebone, regardless of any moral issues, gained his pound of flesh.

Subsequently the plant was dispersed, the stamps going in 1907 to the original Elmore mine at Glasdir, and then still in production.[34] Some 50 years later a brief and unconventional use of the mill site came with its conversion to a Chinese town for the Ingrid Bergman film *Inn of the Sixth Happiness*, which was largely shot in Wales.[35]

A more permanent development began in the mid-1980s when a new owner turned Sygun into a museum and tourist attraction. The main feature is an underground trip into the deep adit and up ladders through old workings to finally emerge onto the mountainside from the Victoria Level. Complete with audio displays, we can only guess what the old miners would have thought, but as an education into their times and working conditions it is an experience not to be missed.

By the bridge over the river, the lower dressing floors including two waterwheels are more evidence of Searell's activities, and a footpath towards Llyn Dinas follows the course of the leat. Outside the adit is a half-scale stamp battery which I made in 1987 but it has since badly rusted from acid waters from the mine. A full size original battery and a concentrating plant are still in use at the Blue Hills tin works at St Agnes in Cornwall, where half an hour will teach you more about crushing and dressing than all the books. But before we leave Sygun, the ruins of Elmore's mill standing against the skyline are worth a glance. Wreathed by the wild rhododendron, they form their own memorial to one of the first flotation plants in the world.

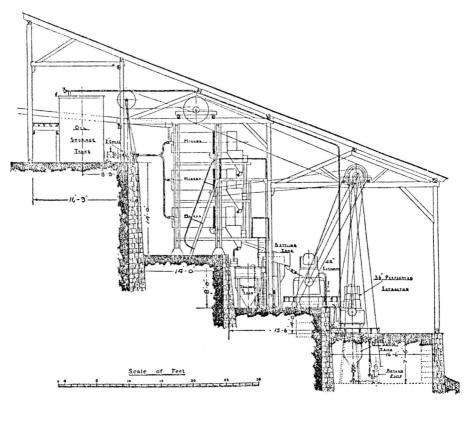

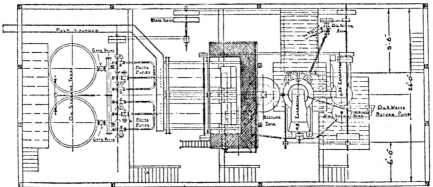

A plan and section of a 50 ton per day Elmore Concentration Plant. The Sygun mill was double this capacity.

6 NANT GWYNANT

The mountains north of Nant Gwynant conceal several sparsely documented workings in ill-defined sets that give rise to many difficulties for the historian and industrial archaeologist. All suffered from high cost of carriage with drought and frost frequently interrupting the crushing and dressing of ore, which in any case was often of too complex a nature readily to be treated by methods available at the time. The ores occur largely at the junction of dissimilar rocks, being richest and most abundant in dark-green pumice-tuffs.[1]

Operations were centred at Hafod-y-porth, Lliwedd, **BRAICH-YR-OEN** (614516) and **HAFOD-Y-LLAN** (623523), Lliwedd being easily the most productive. Of activity in the 18th century, two mining leases have come to light relating to the Hafod-y-Llan estate, which apparently encompassed the hanging valley of Afon Cwm Llan, including Braich-yr-oen :[2]

22nd July, 1762 – Margaret Lynne of Bodysgallen to Hugh Davies for 21 years. 29th September 1794 – Lord Mostyn to Robert Hodgson of Congleton, Edward Hawkins of Macclesfield and Abraham Mills of Hurdsfield.

Braich-yr-oen and Hafod-y-Llan often worked in conjunction, so that ore returned under the latter name may at times have derived from the former; at all events, Hafod-y-llan sold ore at Swansea in 1825/6 and again in 1840.

In the following year the two mines came under the management of Allen Searell, acting for Henry McKellar.[3] Braich-yr-oen was clearly an old work at this period, for in August 1842 Searell recorded, 'Set all the rubbish to clear out of the large excavations and the level Brachyone at £9, subject to be stoped wherever thought proper and paid agreeable to the work done'. None of McKellar's mines turned out to advantage, and from an early stage constant efforts were made to involve other parties, if not to dispose of the speculation altogether.

In 1847 the Hafod-y-Llan property was said to have raised about 150 tons of copper and 30 tons of lead with machinery of the best description on site,[4] and four years later the Hafod-y-Llan Copper and Lead Mines Co. was promoted, presumably by McKellar, but with what outcome is uncertain. In the advertisement reproduced here, the lead mine mentioned is no doubt the one later called Lliwedd-bach, which according to local information was to the north-east above Hafod-y-Llan. It never amounted to much, and comprised one of several trials including Bwlch Mwlchan and Gwastad Annas (660540?) said to have been bedevilled by complex sulphide ores.

After Searell's return in 1856, the impression gained is that McKellar's mining

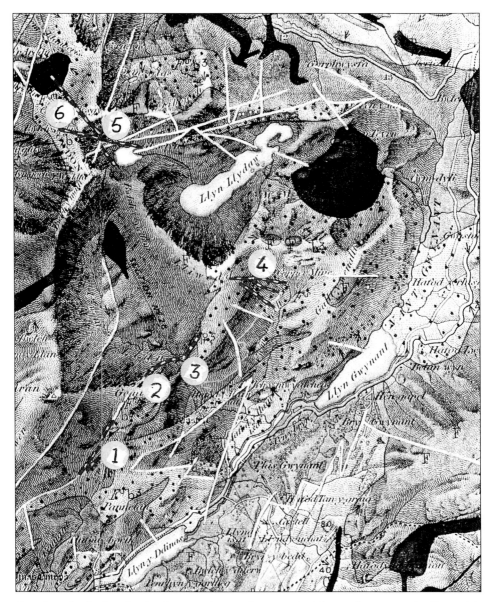

The One-inch Geological map shows the central Snowdon area in the mid-nineteenth century. The lodes are highlighted as broken lines, with faults in white. The dark patches are Greenstone. 1 Hafod-y-Porth; 2, Braich-yr-Oen; Hafod-Y-Llan; 4, Lliwedd; 5, Snowdon; Clogwyn Coch.

HAFOD-Y-LLAN COPPER & LEAD MINES COMPANY,
SITUATED NEAR BEDDGELERT, CARNARVONSHIRE.

Capital £30,000, in shares of £1 each—to be paid up in full upon allotment.

TO BE CONDUCTED ON THE COST-BOOK PRINCIPLE.

COMMITTTEE OF MANAGEMENT.

THOMAS FARNCOMB, Esq , Alderman, Sydenham
NATHANIEL GOULD, Esq., Tavistock-square
HENRY M'KELLAR, Esq., Wandsworth Lodge, Surrey
The Hon. HENRY NOEL, Exton Park, Rutlandshire, and 11, Chandos-street, Cavendish-square
J. WILLIAMS, Esq., M.P. for Macclesfield, Bron Wylfa, St. Asaph, Flintshire
SAMUEL WIX, Esq., Balham-hill, Surrey

BANKERS—Union Bank of London.
CONSULTING MINING ENGINEERS—Messrs. Williams and Noel, Moorgate-street.
SOLICITORS—Messrs. Bischoff and Coxes, 19, Coleman-street.

TEMPORARY OFFICE,—61, MOORGATE-STREET.

The two valuable mineral properties which the Company propose to purchase and work, are Hafod-y-Llan, and Sygun ; the former distant about four miles from Beddgelert, and the latter within a mile from that village. The mineral capabilities of both these properties are well known throughout the Principality. The most important works are now nearly completed, and the mines can be made largely productive in the course of a few months.

The Hafod-y-Llan Copper Mine, comprising a Royalty of upwards of 1500 acres, contains a rich deposit of ore, which is formed by the junction of two smaller lodes with the principal one, thereby increasing its width to 18 feet. A large quantity of ore (a rich yellow sulphuret) has already been raised, and sold at very remunerative prices in Swansea and Liverpool. Other lodes have been opened on this part of the property, showing ore of equal quality with that of the principal lode.

In the Hafod-y-Llan Lead Mine four lodes have been sufficiently opened to prove their productiveness. A comparatively limited sum will be sufficient to bring the mine into an efficient and profitable working state. The last cargo of ore shipped to Liverpool was assayed at 70 per cent. of lead, and 10 ozs. of silver to the ton, but as the workings have become deeper, the improved quality of the ore has increased the assay to 75 per cent.

The Sygun Copper Mine, embracing a royalty of 300 acres, and lying contiguous to the Hafod-y-Llan Estate, has been developed for some years, and contains several good lodes which can be cheaply worked, and for which an early and a liberal return may be anticipated. All the mines can be most economically worked. No steam-power is required ; the valuable machinery now on the mines, for crushing, stamping, and dressing the ore, being driven by water-power, of which there is an abundant supply at all seasons of the year.

The shipping place is Portmadoc, to which there is a good road.

Railways (one 700 yards long) have been laid down, and there are two large water-wheels at Hafod-y-llan and two at Sygun, with offices, storehouses, and workmen's cottages.

The estimates show a net return of upwards of *twenty-seven* per cent. on the capital employed in the completion, and bringing into operation the works now in progress. This return will proportionately increase with the development of new lodes.

After the mines have been fully opened out, it is proposed to pay two-monthly dividends.

The promoters are of opinion that few mining enterprises have been commenced under more auspicious circumstances, and such as will ensure an earlier and a large return to the capital proposed to be embarked.

In order to restrict the liability of the shareholders to the sum paid upon their shares, the Company has been constituted on the Cost-book Principle. There will be no Deed of Settlement.

Applications for shares to be addressed to the " Committee of Management," at their temporary offices, 61, Moorgate-street, where may be had the detailed prospectus, and the reports and estimates of the mining engineers.

Allen Searell. The family was also connected with the Penrecca slate quarries near Buckfastleigh in Devon. *Emyr Searell*

activities, if not slate quarrying, continued in the same desultory fashion with work farmed out wherever opportunity arose. Such an instance occurred in August 1856 when an agreement was made with William Roberts, John Peirce and Morris Parry permitting a search at Braich-yr-oen and 'Llwyedd Bach' lead mine for a period of two months. 'The Tributors shall keep no less than five men constantly at work if the weather Permit or som Actidence hapn. All the Copper and Lead shall be Dressed and fit for Market, The ore to be weighted and Sampled before Leaving the Dressing floor Called Pen y Ceunat (Top of waterfall)....'.

Alongside the waterfall was situated the mill consisting of waterwheels, roller crushers and associated dressing floors, and from it a curious stone-block railway led over a bridge across the river in the direction of Braich-yr-oen. Whether this railway, of which more will be said presently, was in use at the time is uncertain. In June 1857 Searell recorded 'I am in hopes in a few days to have the crushers all right at Hafodyllain, then I think we shall be able to let Brachy Arren at from 4 to 5 shillings in the Pound . . . the last shipment of copper has made a good price and will be an inducement for other parties to take the sett'.

Not only the crushers, however, were in a bad state of repair, for 10 days later Searell continued 'the shoots that take the water to run the wheel are so much Rotten that as soon as the water was turned on to try the Rollers, several of the boards actually fell down'. Another report stated the wheel had been erected about 16 years ago, *ie* about 1841, and used only intermittently. Trials were also in progress elsewhere. 'Am sorry to say Gutter Coch is not turning out much Ore. Pantku is looking just the same as when Mr. Petherick was here, which he did not think much of, but I think the men will make wages at it. Llwydd men are still going on but are not doing much good for themselves'. But by October 1858 there were 'parties willing to take Pantku again at 1/8th of the ore for your portion if you will let it for six or twelve months'. The site of Pantku is said to be high above the road (624504) behind Bryndinas. A year later the rollers collapsed and Searell wanted McKellar to find four or five pounds for repairs in order to crush lead ore, perhaps from Lliwedd-bach.

In April 1862 Braich-yr-oen was tried again, apparently after a long interlude, for Searell wrote 'I have this day been at Braich-yr-oen and set four men to drive the level, it took them all day yesterday to clear the mouth...'.

A few men were also scratching about at Braich-yr-arran for copper and lead, but McKellar considered 'the price is not tempting for copper just now. You may perchance find some Gold with the quartz there is elsewhere on the property. You will recollect *Mr. Calvert found in one part 17 dwt* +10 grams at Sygun, as also at Hafod y Llan of which I have samples'. This was a period of considerable speculation in 'gold mines' throughout Britain, and Calvert who found the precious metal with suspiciously little difficulty, was remembered for his book *The Gold Rocks of Great Britain and Ireland.*

Although no longer a young man, Searell was still leading a hard life, as can be glimpsed from a letter to McKellar in April 1862. 'I did not get yours of yesterday till 6pm on my return from Hafod y llain. I started at 5am and intended to be back soon enough to get my letters and reply by this days post but the rain had fallen so much that the River was so full I could not before it abated'. Years of toil and disappointment were disheartening him, and he admitted a sentiment the truth of which few miners would willingly deny. 'The copper at Braich yr Oen is improving, think I had better keep the men on it this week. I should like to get Captain Julian to see both the Lead lode and Braich yr Oen before I do much more, as I have no confidence in my own judgement in mining, I really do not understand it, for it rarely ever turns out the way I expected'.

Julian found strings of copper in the long level a few fathoms from a crosscut to the west, but nothing came of the discovery. There were then about fifteen men employed at the mines and slate quarry.[5] The old vision of a railway to the coast lingered, but nothing resulted beyond a mineral line from the quarry with a spectacular incline down towards the road near Hafod-y-llan farmhouse, probably built in the 1870s. D.C. Davies, writing in 1877, recorded how 'the South Snowdon waggon with a fine team of horses traverses the road between the quarry and Portmadoc, a distance of eleven miles daily.'[6]

After McKellar's death in 1862, and Searell's in 1865, the next reference to Braich-yr-oen occurs in 1883 when it was under trial by Thomas Green, John Green and W.E. Parry, with five men underground.[7] D.C. Davies reported in February 1884 that storms had washed away the blacksmith's shop and dressing floors, and he referred to a fine course of ore already proved. But two years later the mine was officially 'suspended'.

The remaining mine in the area is **HAFOD-Y-PORTH** (611506), sundry workings that seem never to have rewarded the adventurers with success in spite of considerable developments dating at least from 1755.[8] Details of ninety years later come from an advertisement when the Bulkeley Mine Co. offered the plant for unreserved sale on 8th April 1845.[9] The equipment included a 22ft x 3ft waterwheel and 24-inch rolls, nearly new, an 8-head stamp-battery and 10 tons of 'T' rails.

Presumably McKellar also took up this sett in view of Searell's references to 'Brachy Arren' or Braich-y-arran, this being a geographical name in the close vicinity. From

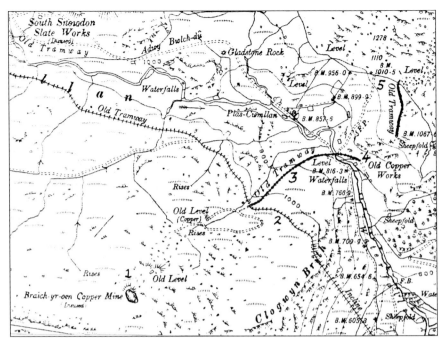

The second edition 6 inch Ordnance map shows, 1; Braich yr Oen; 2,tramway from South Snowdon quarries (top left); 3, stone-block tramroad; 4, Hafod-y-Llan mill and mine.

these workings bereft of machinery, ore was dragged over the mountain to Hafod-y-Llan mill.

In 1864 the sett was taken up by the Hafod y Porth Copper Mining Co. Some ore was sold at Swansea and a turbine-driven crusher came under consideration.[10] Returns revived in 1868/9, and in 1873 a prospectus appeared for the Great Aran & Snowdon Copper Mines. The accompanying plan showed no less than nine lodes intersecting, with a further four near Hafod-y-porth farmhouse – the majority of which amounted to little more than a gleam in the promoters' eyes[11]

Thereafter a succession of companies tried, with never more than a few men at a time. In 1882-4 the mine was named Maudslay after the owner or lessee, the agent being Charles Kneebone. This failing, the usual subterfuge to mislead unwary investors, that is, a further change of title, manifested itself in the appellation Aran and Snowdon, the owner being quoted as L.D. Bunn of Dawlish.[7]

By 1888 the name Aran sufficed for the next owner E.H. Harmont, who with Kneebone held the property until the North Wales United Mines Co. took over briefly in 1890.[7] Whether some of these ventures ever put a spade in the ground is questionable, and thus by degrees Hafod-y-porth faded into oblivion.

The cart track to South Snowdon quarries, now a popular route to the summit of Snowdon, makes a convenient approach to the mines just described. On the left is the impressive quarry incline, and across the river where the track comes close to

Hafod-y-Llan mill is close to a popular route up Snowdon. The course of the tramroad and leat appear as the curving paths, top left.   *David Bick*

Afon Llan is a miner's path with steps formed of large stone flags and leading to Hafod-y-Llan mill with the ruins of a large wheelpit and crusher-house. There is also evidence of a smaller waterwheel, perhaps for working stamps, near the mill in a large ore-dressing area which is on made-up ground and retained by a high wall above the river.

On a precipitous mountainside are the opencut workings and levels of Hafod-y-Llan, from which a narrow-gauge tramway with wooden sleepers conveyed ore along an embankment ending in a pier, to be discharged down a slide to the mill.

The mill derived its power via a leat above a waterfall where a row of trial workings can be seen. A very puzzling feature is a long line of stone blocks forming the sleepers of another tramroad from the direction of Braich-yr-oen, already mentioned. The route curves steeply up the mountainside though the bridge over the river has long since vanished. Due to shifting ground measurements of the gauge vary, but something between 4ft and 4ft 4 inches is the probable figure – a width by the way, which the output of no British copper mine could ever have justified.

The stone-block railway apparently terminated just above the later quarry tramway which crosses its formation. Towards Braich-yr-oen appear two more embankments and high piers, leading us to suppose that ore wheeled or trammed from the mine was shot down slides prior to transferring to tram-waggons. However, such a clumsy and labour-intensive solution is hardly conceivable, unless designed by a committee.

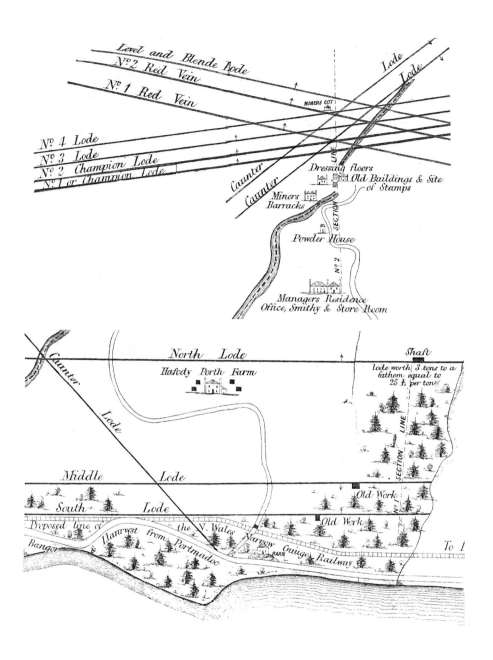

A tempting promotional plan of Hafod-y-Porth issued in 1873. Most of the features can still be traced including the 'miner's cot', now a roofless ruin. Note the proposed railway which was never built.

George Hall fills his carbide lamp before exploring an adit at Hafod-y-Porth in 1957. *David Bick*

An abortive level at Hafod-y-Porth with wrought-iron bar rails, probably dating from the 1840s. *David Bick*

Perhaps the upper portions were added as a make-shift to work in conjunction with the stone-block line that was never completed.

The mill must date from before Searell's time, and no doubt the railway also. But old technologies die hard and it is dangerous to dogmatise without firm evidence. As an example, I have seen in the 1960s a wooden railway laid down and used at Cynnant, a virgin lead mine north of Llandovery.[12]

A deep excavation faulted at both ends identifies the mine of Braich-yr-oen, and must have yielded large quantities of ore. Fifty years ago the adit was still open, with 2 or 3 cwt of zinc blende dumped outside, some being of a transparent variety.

Over the flank of Aran lies Hafod-y-porth, marked by a profusion of trial shafts and levels evident over a wide area. Apart from the remnants of a mill and various other buildings, a peculiar feature noticed in 1957 was a 19 inch-gauge mineral line emerging from an adit, consisting of bar-rails morticed directly into wooden sleepers. Though the

MINING MATERIALS FOR SALE IN CARNARVONSHIRE.

TO BE SOLD BY AUCTION,

(*Without the least Reserve,*)

On Tuesday, the 8th day of April, 1845, at the hour of Eleven o'clock, at the Bulkeley Mines, on Havod-y-porth Lands, near Beddgelert,

THE whole of the Mining Materials belonging to the Bulkeley Mine Co., consisting of a 22 Feet Water-wheel, 3 Feet Breast, Crushing Mill, nearly new, with 24 Inch Rolls, Stamps, with 8 Heads, about 10 Tons of T Pattern rolled Iron Rails, Sheet-iron, Waggons, Smiths' Bellows, Anvils, Miners' Tools, Iron, Timber, &c.

dumps displayed lead, zinc, traces of copper minerals and an abundance of iron-stained rock, there was a general air of poverty about the site which underground exploration amply confirmed; nevertheless an interesting mine and worth the effort to see.

High on a wild and remote mountainside, the most productive mine in the area was **LLIWEDD** (634531), with the inevitable variations in spelling. It was sometimes known as Bwlch Mulchan after the farm on which it lies. The area was part of the extensive Craflwyn Estate near Beddgelert, which had belonged to the Parry family for generations. The Old Series one inch geological map shows a 'Copper Mine' at the head of Cwm Erch with three lodes running more or less east-west, but it seems that only one or two were productive.[13a]

Lliwedd was returning copper ore in 1806, and after about 1821 was worked by the Lliwedd Mining Co, a rather shaky concern consisting mainly of shopkeepers and businessmen from Ruthin.[13b] At times they included a draper, a butcher and a currier, who like the mine captains came and went, but somehow production largely held up for the next 25 years. Most of the ore was sold at Swansea, but much was destined elsewhere including Liverpool and the Mona smelting works on Anglesey. When Parry died about 1829 he bequeathed his estate to Sir John Duckinfield of Berkshire and a naval captain, Thomas Garth from Wiltshire. However, the rents and royalties were to go to his four unmarried daughters. Duckinfield's agent was John Hughes a solicitor who was also employed by the Bishop of Bangor.

In 1831 a new level had been driven 'near the bottom of all the works', but endless trouble arose over leases and delays in payments of royalties, which amounted to $1/8$th of net sales. Sir John complained more than once that he did not know who the partners were, or even if the mine was still at work. Of the five original partners in March 1834, two were bankrupt and one dead. 'Hugh Davies we know is insolvent and Mr Roberts is the only respectable man of the number'.

Duckinfield died in 1836 and two years later Joseph Peers of Ruthin became the sole lessee and company solicitor. Output now greatly increased, amounting to 1090 tons to Swansea alone between 1838 and 1843. Peers claimed he had spent nearly £5000 on the mine – a vast sum in those days, and it is probably during this period that the crushing mills as described later, were erected.

But soon after, Lliwedd was in trouble and the manager, Anthony Marsden, wrote to Hughes that unless the royalty on poor ores was reduced they could not pay at all. He gave some revealing figures as to costs, but from later sales of even poorer ores it seems that the sums were exaggerated. However, the appeal did not prevent Marsden's dismissal shortly afterwards.

Costs per ton	£ s d
Mining	1 5 0
Dressing	1 0 0
Carriage to Portmadoc	1 2 3
Harbour dues & shipping	1 6
Freight to Liverpool	5 0
	£ 3 19 3

Lliwedd. The upper picture shows the two crushing mills, and paved dressing floors on the left. Below, are a pair of fluted crushing rolls, much worn, and segments of a waterwheel.

A new phase began with the arrival of the Sneyds, wealthy landowners from Basford Hall near Leek in Staffordshire. The family had already lost money in mining and copper smelting, but an acute want of business sense did not prevent further speculation, this time in nearby Snowdon. The aim was presumably a source of ore for their furnaces – see next chapter. They also plunged headlong into Lliwedd, sub-leasing it from Joseph Peers on very improvident terms. Both investments were soon bitterly regretted, and as early as June 1844 the Reverend John Sneyd wrote to Hughes 'I am sorry to inform you that the mine has turned out a very bad adventure'. And there was again trouble over a lease, with Laura Parry bewailing the lack of royalities which were spoiling her plans for a longer stay in Paris.

A year later the Sneyds were desperate for release at almost any price. After having entered 'a most unwise bargain' with Peers, their losses already exceeded £2,000 and they were sickened by 'the knavery of the common miners and rascality of the Petty Courts'. The misses Parry, or some of them, were now in Germany and still demanding a royalty of $1/8$th. Such arrangements, based on sales and not profits were commonplace, but fatal to a mine in difficulty. With the best ores running 12 per cent copper worth nearly £8 per ton having been long exhausted, the grades were now much poorer. Forty three tons sent to Anglesey and worth £149, brought in only £87 after carriage and royalties – a mere £2 per ton. Closure was inevitable.

By July 1846 the mine 'had been for many months abandoned', but the Sneyds were still legally entangled with Joseph Peers four years later. We do not know how the sorry tale ended, but although the above tells us little about the mine itself, it illustrates all too well the human hopes, intrigues and tragedies that mere technical details and statistics can never reveal.

Such as they were, Lliwedd's best days had gone, and copper, which had been falling ever since the Napoleonic wars, continued down in price; the income which had bolstered the lifestyle of the Parry maidens for over 30 years was almost at an end. In 1853, Lliwedd Mawr, presumably so named to distinguish it from Lliwedd Bach, was offered for sale, it being optimistically claimed that 200 men could be employed on the copper ore in sight[14]. It was eventually taken up by a new company involving Robert Roberts of Geuffos, Llanddulas, Rhyl; whether this was the same man who had caused so much trouble at Sygun many years before, is uncertain. In any case, early in 1858 he described the mine as having been in a most disorderly manner, but much had since been done, with 'a new vein lately found across the others very promising and the ore is about 3 feet wide though not quite pure throughout'. Henry Mckellar of Sygun may also have been involved; both Lliwedds were later reported on Bwlch Mwlchan land, and this would explain Searell's references to these mines only after his return in 1856.[15] In March 1860 he recorded that Captain Julian had visited Lliwedd and was likely to take it.

According to the 1867 *Mineral Statistics,* mines then at work included Llwydd-bach (copper and lead), agent Mr. Searle, also 'Llwydd-Maw or Gelliwen', agent John Clift, proprietor W.F. Brand. In another section 'Llywydd' is quoted as returning nearly 6 tons of copper ore, this being its last appearance in official statistics.

After World War II, the late S. Dawson Ware spent much effort trying to revive copper mining in Snowdonia, and recorded that the South African Gold Mining

Syndicate investigated Lliwedd in 1900, the manager being a Mr. Frazer. In 1950, Ware corresponded with Owen Williams of Blaenau Ffestiniog, who replied that about 40 years previously he had worked at Lliwedd. 'There was an old cart track that was in use then to transport the copper down. No machinery whatever were used then, just the simple picking and washing, then placed in sacks and carried down to Portmadoc to be placed in boats and taken to Swansea. The copper was a blue colour with very little sulphur.' [16]

When exploring underground in 1952 I came across a newspaper dated 1907 and whilst in Beddgelert a few years later encountered a 70 year old miner named Roberts. He had worked in Brittania, Sygun and Lliwedd, and referred to two feet of good ore in a trial shaft 4 yards deep near the mine, also good peacock-ore in an opencast near the stream.

Because of crevass-like opencuts testifying to the value of ore extracted and the wealth of old machinery, Lliwedd is of more than common interest. A cart track leads to a crusher-house, to which ore was fed down a steep stone-lined chute. From the top of the chute a short built-up path leads to the main adit where rusting remains of trams repose on an 18 inch gauge line of 'T' rails in cast-iron chairs. Higher up are spectacular and dangerous vertical open-workings three or four feet wide and of great depth, showing here and there ribs of copper ore. Alongside are extensive waste-tips, with much hand-cobbed material.

The crushing mill is ruinous but reveals a waterwheel in pieces, made by the Hawarden Iron Works. The floor has collapsed, making it hard to fathom the mechanical arrangements. At least one pair of rolls are within, and a set of fluted rolls lying nearby prompts the question whether the plant comprised two or even three pairs, similar to the illustration under Dolawen mine (see chapter 8). Multiple roller mills were virtually unknown in Wales, and therefore that one might survive even in this condition is a stroke of remarkable fortune. Perhaps a partial or even complete restoration may eventually be possible.

Below the mill is a dressing-floor paved with slabs, and another mill building with a 30ft x 6ft 6 inch wheelpit but apparently never used. Other ironwork lying about includes stamp-heads and rolls, much worn and wasted. On a higher level are components of a ponderous 11ft diameter cast-iron flywheel of dowelled rim segments, its purpose unknown.

Tumbledown remnants of other buildings including offices and a smithy are also in the vicinity. Dating the various features has yet to be attempted but lack of documentary evidence makes the task very difficult. A survey of Lliwedd has been undertaken by the Snowdonia National Park Study Centre. I do not think any other mine in Wales epitomizes to a greater extent the determination and spirit of the 'old men' and it would be a fitting memorial if something could be done to save the site, remote though it is.

Before leaving the Gwynant region, intrusive rocks at the head of Cwm-Llan are worth mentioning. They are rich in copper where purple-coloured in streaks and patches, and include chalcocite, plush-red cuprite and occasional copper-pyrites and malachite.[17]

In past ages it might have been supposed that the copper lodes of Snowdon were created by the gods to taunt men, for a more desolate and inhospitable situation could scarcely be imagined. At all events, physical obstacles did not deter, and perhaps the romantic setting even encouraged a succession of companies to almost inevitable disaster.

In 1798/1801, Bingley wrote that **SNOWDON** (616547) had been discovered only a few years previously.[1a,1b] Great were the expectations, and Sir Robin Williams the lessor, thought that 'our fortunes are made (if we) only spend enough money'. One of the men involved wanted 'a spot of land to build a house upon with a bit of garden' closer to the works, but whether he did so is not clear.[1c] Barracks were soon erected and in the winter of 1801 the miners had to cut a tunnel through snow to reach the level, the drifts being up to 20 yds deep in many places.

A postcard view of the Brittania mill across Llyn Llydaw. The mine was on the slopes of Snowdon, the two being joined by an aerial ropeway. *C J Williams*

Ore was certainly being sold by 1804, and a year later a tourist recorded how a four-mile track from the summit to the Saracen's Head (later the Snowdon Ranger) on the shore of Llyn Cwellyn 'has lately been made to bring down the copper ore on sledges which is found at a great height in the mountains. These sledges, drawn by two horses, will carry six hundredweight, and we saw an old man of seventy who is daily employed with a couple of poor animals in this toilsome occupation'.[2] Ore was humped on men's backs a thousand feet from the far side to the top of Snowdon, and by cart from the Saracen's Head to Caernarvon.[3]

At a somewhat later date the new road from Llanberis to Pen-y-Gwryd proved a better route, and the well-known Miners' Track was built to join it at Pen-y-Pass. Richard Fenton the antiquarian descended this way from Snowdon in August 1813.

The mine forwarded ore to Swansea and probably elsewhere for fifteen years between 1804 and 1842, but more especially in the earlier period. About 1811 it came to one of many stops due to transport costs and the climate.[4a] In 1844 the Sneyd family, who we have already encountered at Lliwedd, became lessees of the Snowdon concern, another adventure which cost them dearly. A diary kept by John William Sneyd, a young man of twenty-two, reveals that on 3 July his father ordered a deep adit to be driven above the upper lake.[4b] This was presumably the one later named Sneyd's level; another was Pascoe's level, after William Pascoe of Beddgelert who was engaged as mine captain shortly afterwards. He had earlier worked at Llwyndu. There were several mentions of an 'enginehouse' where ore was kept and an 'engine' appeared in reports to the *The Mining Journal* in the 1850s; what was meant is uncertain, probably a crushing mill – there is no evidence of a steam engine at the mine.

On one occasion the Reverend John Sneyd addressed the miners on a religious theme, but what it availed them in the English language which few could understand, we can scarcely imagine. At all events it did not prevent, and perhaps even encouraged, a law case claiming wages at a cost to the company of nearly £400. But there were lighter moments when on 30 August father and son ventured to the top of Snowdon to see the sun set; they stayed all night and saw it rise in the morning. In the same

---

CWMDYLE ROCK AND GREEN LAKE.—At Pascoe's level, No. 1 stope is still yielding a large quantity of ore ; the lode is about 9 ft. wide. I have set on another pare to stope in the back of the end going east, just under the large stope, where we find some good ore. I hope to be able to give more particulars as to this stope next week. At Price's level, in No. 1 stope, the lode is 2½ ft. wide, producing some rich stones of copper. We have been clearing the copper we have broken the past week in the stopes in the bottoms of the level ; consequently, we have not broken any ground. At No. 5 level, in No. 2 stope, the lode is 6 ft. wide, producing some good stones of copper. At No. 6 level, in No. 1 stope, the lode is still as productive as it has been for the last fortnight. At No. 2 stope we have a good course of ore on the south wall. No. 3 stope is improved, and presenting every indication of again making a good course of ore. At No. 7 level we are breaking a large quantity of good ore ; and, from the appearance of the lode, there is every reason to expect a large deposit of ore in this level. We are still waiting the arrival of the wheels for the engine, which have been faithfully promised to-morrow (June 28). If so, we shall at once commence crushing, and ship another cargo of ore next week

A typical weekly report in *The Mining Journal*, 2nd July 1853.

No. 4 Level, showing stopes and heavy timbering above. Beautiful blue and green encrustations from copper salts adorn the workings.   *Jon Knowles*

This boxed-in launder descending through No. 2 Level is a mystery; it may have conveyed partially broken ore from higher workings.   *Jon Knowles*

A boxed-in orepass No. 3 Level descending through the workings.   *Jon Knowles*

A high stope in No. 4 Level.   *Jon Knowles*

month 34 tons of ore were conveyed via the Trent and Mersey Canal to the Whiston Copper Works south of Leek; these had been established in 1770 to smelt rich ore from the nearby Ecton mines, which were by now almost exhausted.[4c] About 1820 the works had come into the hands of three Sneyd brothers who also owned the Mixon copper mine, but freightage from Snowdon must have eaten heavily into profits.

Later in 1844 the Sneyds walked to Lliwedd and the 'Buckley Mine' (Hafod y Porth) to measure tram-wagons, and on 1 November John Taylor the well known mining engineer and manager paid a visit; he was unimpressed and the company quietly faded away.

Nonetheless, in spite of the record and its Siberian climate, Snowdon again verified the maxim that regardless of its true potential, whenever a mine stood the least chance of exploiting, there would be those out to exploit it. A new revival came in 1847 as Snowdon and Dalawin Copper Mines, the latter being near Bethesda as mentioned later. According to the description, Snowdon had six levels, stamps and two sets of grinders, and a 40ft diameter waterwheel. A road to the crusher-house had been built at great expense.[5]

To what extent the venture prospered is uncertain, but in June 1850 shares came on offer in the Snowdon Copper Mines with twenty-four men at work. Winzes were being sunk in Pascoe's Level and between Rowland's and Sneyd's Levels. A few weeks later the crusher began operating and two levels were said to be driving, one from the shore of Glaslyn and another beneath it.[6]

More is known of the next attempt, commenced by the Cwm Dyle Rock and Green Lake Copper Mining Co. in September 1851.[7] A London management reported 'the purchase of interest of the late adventurers on very favourable terms and the grant covered a huge area of about 15 square miles. The seven levels were No.1, Sneyd's, 60 fathoms long; 2, Rowlands, 12 fathoms; 3, Pascoe's, 80 fathoms; 4, Price's, 100 fathoms; and 5, 6 and 7, all about 15 fathoms long. Pascoe's yielded the best ore, claimed to be 10% copper over a width of 14-20 inches solid.

Smelting furnaces were soon in course of erection with much emphasis on the anticipated economies of using peat as a fuel. The miners included Welsh, French and Belgians and in May 1852 an advertisement appeared for a mine captain 'preferably able to speak French' – communication with the rest of the men presumably being considered unnecessary. The job was given to Thomas Colliver from Cornwall, who had been on the mine since February 1852, if not before.

Materials from Dolawen mine were arriving by the autumn, and the crusher and stamps were constantly at work. There was however no mention of the furnaces, the intention of concentrating if not wholly reducing the ore to reduce transport cost having failed to mature. Early in 1853 a new 33ft diameter waterwheel and 36 head of stamps were in course of erection, and Llyn Llydaw was lowered to assist in building a causeway across its eastern end, the task being completed later in the year. Twenty men were constructing miners' cottages, but on inspection Captain Matthew Francis of Cardiganshire found little encouraging to say.

Something approaching the true state of affairs came out at the A.G.M. in March 1854, when Mr. Sewell the chairman presented a balance sheet. He admitted to a confused state in the accounts, which had been debited as much as £16,059, ostensibly for the cost of the mine. It also became clear that in the beginning the scene resembled a shambles, with the crusher-house and machinery partly destroyed and missing, levels blocked up, and no means of getting ore from the mountain except on men's backs – different indeed from the glowing prospectus. And in spite of recent assertions of over 180 men employed, the small number of hands was now blamed for delays. In short, a warning to credulous shareholders to take the publicity in the mining press with a substantial pinch of salt. Colliver had laboured under great difficulties with little credit available; without capital for inclined planes, tramways, ore-shoots and machinery he could promise nothing.

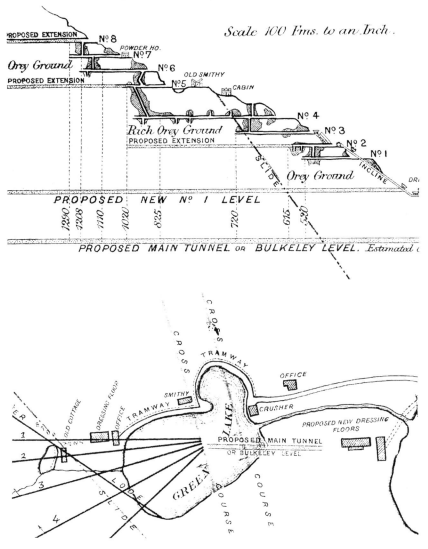

Extracts from plans accompanying the Great Snowdon Copper company of 1873

The mine struggled on, with one lode being worked at the water's edge, and during very bad weather in April 1854 a boat actually sank *twice* in crossing the lake. A tramway 323 fathoms in length was thereupon begun round the eastern end from the stamps to the crushers, where two new sets of rolls went to work in July. By the end of 1854, ore worth £2,550 had been sold to Swansea, but thereafter the mine went from bad to worse.

The winter of 1855/6 proved very severe, snow and ice burying the surface for months on end. At the March A.G.M. it was announced that Colliver had resigned and was threatening Chancery proceedings to recover monies due. The wooden shoots from the upper levels to the stamps had collapsed or been wantonly pulled down, and in March 1856 Thomas & Co. the Caernarvon engineers were suing for machinery supplied. Overwhelmed by circumstances, the company came to an ignominious fate and subsequent adventurers reaped the benefit of the heavy outlay in tramways, roads and other essentials.

The mine was sold by order of the Vice-Chancellor in the summer of 1857, but hardly was the corpse cold before being resurrected in the form of the Cwmdyle Copper Mining Co., with £2,000 capital and offices at the British Hotel, Bangor. The chairman was Hedworth Lee, a civil engineer.

Under the somewhat premature heading 'Another Successful Recuscitation', *The Mining Journal* announced that 'real friends of mining will be glad to learn the property is likely to prove equal to the representations of the most saguine reporters'. The investors were mainly local and the lessor, R. Williams Bulkeley of Baron Hill, Beaumaris, subscribed £200 which he later increased to £450.[8]

Early in 1859 the ore was fetching £17 per ton at Amlwch, and in the 12 months ending September 1861 ore worth £2,933 had been sold, allowing the novelty of a dividend. Perhaps the effort was too great, since this 'extensive and highly productive copper mine' came up for auction on 15th April 1863, 'a further yet moderate outlay of capital being all that is necessary to render it one of the largest and most profitable in the Principality'. But it appears that no takers were found, for in August 1864 the directors advertised for £3,000 to develop the works. Whether or not the appeal succeeded, Cwm Dyle again came under the auctioneer's hammer on 18th January 1865 at the British Hotel Bangor, with the same verbal enticement that had failed two years before.

As to what happened next I am uncertain, but on 25th May 1871 the mine, worked by the Snowdon Copper Mining Co. Ltd., was offered for sale in one lot without reserve at the Penypass Inn. The plant included crushers, stamps, wagons, tramways, inclines, engine shed, and a 30ft x 3ft 3ins waterwheel, with a lease running for 26 years at 1/16 royalty.

Apparently Edmund Spargo was the purchaser.[9] He acquired the lease in 1872 and continued operations in conjunction with Ezra Jenks Coates, and in March 1873 launched The Great Snowdon Copper Mining Co. Ltd. with a nominal capital of £120,000.[10] Sir Richard Williams Bulkeley again numbered among the directors, who now included George Gowland, Chairman of the Original Hartlepools Colliery Co. A highly coloured prospectus quoted opinions from Robert Etheridge F.R.S., F.G.S., and Thomas Julian of Rhosesmor Mines, late of Simdde Dylluan and Great

Wheal Vor. Much was made of extensive halvans amounting to 50,000 tons of low-grade ore, plus intentions of driving a level beneath Green Lake (Glaslyn). The halvans consisted merely of waste with a sprinkling of copper, but with its typically short memory the investing public was once again deceived.

In June 1873 the company advertised for a secondhand 40ft x 4ft waterwheel and an agent at £120 annual salary, Spargo himself taking the position of manager in April 1874. On 24th August he submitted a progress report which referred to a

An orepass in No. 4 Level.   *Jon Knowles*

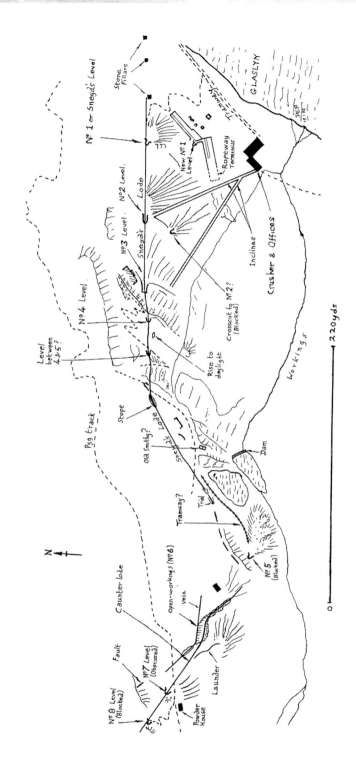

The Industrial Archaeology of Snowdon, based on a survey by Alasdair Neill in 1979. The new No. 1 Level was probably driven by the Brittania company

The Brittania mill, probably about 1914.   *P J Appleton*

The ruins of Brittania mill looking across Llyn Llydaw.

relaid tramway from the crusher round the lake to the incline, and new launders from the lake to the crusher-wheel.[11] There were also new barracks and dressing-floors with machinery supplied by George Green of Aberystwyth, a new cart-road 546 yds long from the crusher-house to the barracks, and a new dam at Glaslyn 9ft high and 40ft long. Other work included new crusher-rolls and general repairs to the buildings, as well as mending the road to Penypass and restoring no less than 133 culverts in 2 miles. On the vital question of ore reserves there was little of material benefit to say.

The halvans proved worthless, and early in 1875 a Special General Meeting revealed the company's grave predicament. The board was now said to be concentrating on reducing the capital and re-arranging the amount paid to vendors (probably including Spargo), reducing director's fees and London management expenses. But in April 1875 a decision to wind up finally settled the venture's fate.

Extravagances, if not downright frauds such as these, were familiar enough and it is worth pausing for a moment to recall the words of D.C. Davies written only a year or two later, 'If we imagine a company formed in London, with a lord for its chairman, and a general and a colonel among its directors, with a managing director, a secretary, and a consulting referee, in order to manage and carry on an ordinary grocery business in a small country town, we have supposed something that is not a whit more ridiculous than are the confederations frequently established to work good little mines but which, at the most, cannot yield more than the profits of a grocery business.' [12]

Now followed an intermission until 1888, when Edward Herzberg Harmont, 58 Lombard Street, London, became lessee.0[13] He had other mining interests in the area, and spent £38,000 in eight years before going bankrupt.[14] George Charles Howard a stock broker was also involved, and Charles Kneebone acted as agent.

In 1890 the North Wales United Mines Co. Ltd was formed to work Snowdon, West Snowdon and Great Aran, and shareholders included Lionel Mozley, Lovel

The end of a beer barrel found in No.5 level.
Jon Knowles

Latham, A.E. Young, C.E. Strich and W.H. Barber.[15] The agent was Arthur Canning. This company operated until 1897, but in spite of employing up to 42 miners and 35 men at surface, it sold no ore at all – that is, if the *Mineral Statistics* are to be believed.

The last and best known working is attributable to the Brittania Copper Mine Ltd., 4 Bishopsgate, London. The company was formed in March 1898 with a nominal capital of £90,000 and in 1901 the directors included George Charles Howard, Sydney Hunt and Percy John Ogle, consulting engineer.[16]

The board embarked upon a programme of capital expenditure involving a costly new mill and a manager's house on the shore of Llyn Llydaw, to which a long aerial ropeway built in 1898 led from the mine beyond Glaslyn, thus in effect, reducing the transport problems by nearly a mile and avoiding the steep climb between the lakes.[17]

The dressing plant went into operation in the spring of 1899 and the record output over a two-year period (1208 tons) must have reflected the discovery of a good bunch of ore. Nevertheless a decline followed, and the combined effect of copper prices so low that few mines could weather brought work to a standstill by 1904.

In spite of the clear impossibility of profit under such circumstances, further money was somehow raised and activity re-commenced in 1907 under a Cornishman, C. Vercoe.[13] Electricity generated by a waterwheel is said to have powered the dressing floors, and the crushing plant was powered by a Pelton Wheel under a 550ft head of water conveyed by pipeline from Glaslyn.[18] The road to the mine was at this period good enough for motor cars. The returns amounted to only 124 tons of ore in 1913. The Penypass Copper Co. took over in 1915 in which year new plant was added, but not even improved prices arising from the First World War availed.[13] When work ceased a year later, it was for the last time.

Old cottages and ore-stores at Penypass, the Brittania Mill and remnants of earlier activities around the shores of Glaslyn, testify to over a century's endeavour. Yet it was not entirely wasted, for the miners' tracks and paths have for generations smoothed the way to the summit of the highest mountain in Wales.[19]

More inaccessible, and close to Llyn Du'r Arddu, **CLOGWYN COCH** (603556) seems also to have begun towards the end of the 18th century. It usually operated in conjunction with Llanberis two miles to the north, the miners being employed at the upper site in the summer and the lower in the winter.[20] Occasionally however, it worked all the year round, when extra blankets were provided in the barracks.[21]

In 1830, five levels were active, and in January 1831 Rowland Philip was fined 2/6d for breaking a wagon on an inclined plane, the remains of which still feature prominently at the site.[22] The mine was at work in the 1850s and '60s and in 1873 following a favourable report by Nicholas Ennor, Edmund Spargo attempted a reopening.[23]

According to Robert Hunt's statistics, Clogwyn returned ore in the years 1822, 29, 30, 38, 39 and 1867, amounting to 191 tons. But this can only represent a portion, most of which went elsewhere, or was included with Llanberis.

Rumour has it that Snowdon and Clogwyn communicated underground, but this has not been confirmed; it is also said the refreshment hut at the top of Snowdon was originally opened by a miner from Clogwyn Coch.[24a]

Near the head of Llyn Peris is **LLANBERIS** (597587) a mine more productive than profitable, with beginnings about the middle of the 18th century although it may be

This cast iron stamp-head lies among the rubble at Clogwyn Coch.
C J Williams

very much older.[24b] At that time the present road was but a horse-path, boats on the lake offering the only practical means of conveying heavy materials and ore.

The mine formed part of the Vaynol Estate, and the following details from a report dated 9th August 1760 reveal something of its history and main areas of activity.[25]

Lower Works
Trials were made in three places and levels driven but good ore at surface proved a disappointment in depth. After several successive attempts the trials were abandoned.

Yew Tree Works
Ore was discovered towards the north-west near a yew tree, and soon afterwards there followed a further discovery to the south, on the same lode. 'The works were carried on in both places till the same were cut into each other and met together, and in these two works which are now united and called the Yewtree Works the substance of the Ore has been got which has been sold from the Llanberis Mine. These works extend betwixt 50 and 60 yards in length the Ore lying at the Bottom all the length thereof . . . A shaft is sunk about 10 yards Deep lower than the floor of these Works, the Ore having continued all the Depth...'

Smithy Works
These were south east of the Yew Tree works and lower down the mountain supposedly on the same vein, but little exploration had so far been carried out.

Bridge Works
'The Direction of the Vein of Ore in the Yewtree Works pointed through the Smithy Works to this place where the Ore was found near the Bridge'.

The Bridge works were about 200 yds from the Yewtree works, and about 50 yards above the lake, the bridge being on the road to Nant Peris. From this description the whole area of activity did not exceed two or three hundred yards from end to end.

The Rev. Archdeacon Ellis of Bangor became involved in a number of industrial speculations including mines near Bethesda and Llanrwst, and by 1778 was running

Llanberis together with his son Hugh Ellis and William Bridge.[26] The latter two were later very active in Dinorwic Quarry.

Boats conveyed the ore along Llyn Peris and were loaded from a wooden staging or jetty, which a watercolour by John 'Warwick' Smith commemorated in 1792. Towards the end of the century Charles Roe & Co. of Macclesfield took up Llanberis, although with little or no success. Precipitation pits were used, and the company also tried roasting the ore. A contemporary description is given by Aitkin.[27]

> This mine consists of several horizontal galleries driven into Snowdon; the rock is hard whin and hornblende schiztus, the matrix quartz; the metal is a rich yellow ore, containing copper in unison with sulphur, the quantity procured is not very considerable .... The stamping mill consists of fixed oaken beams shod with iron and placed perpendicularly side by side along a large trough; these beams are alternately raised by a waterwheel

Such machines were incredibly noisy and I well remember the mill at Wheal Martha or New Consols, near Callington, with its stamp-battery fifty years ago. Not only was conversation impossible, but not a sound appeared to issue from the manager's lips, though shouting at the top of his voice. It was one of the last ever erected in this country, probably in the world, and there is always a certain sadness in seeing an invention that for centuries has served its purpose well, consigned at last to the limbo of history.

From 1805 Thomas Wright of Nantwich leased the mine, and in 1812 the principal level was about 200yds long with at the end an immense lofty cavern and workings extending to a depth of 100ft beneath.[28] Wright relinquished his interests in 1821, but if the Swansea returns are any guide his tenure proved a failure for only 60 tons were returned, in 1816.

In 1821 the lease passed to William and Thomas Jones of Wrexham, and regular substantial returns commenced two years later. This is a very interesting period, involving the construction of a fine masonry aqueduct of numerous arches crossing the valley from near the site of the stamps battery.[29] It conveyed the waters of Afon Dudodyn to work a new pumping and stamping wheel at a level situated a little over a quarter of a mile southeast of the old main adit at Dol-Ithel. These workings were entirely separate, and with little doubt contributed largely to output during the next twenty years or so. Richard Fenton referred to a new level 180 yds long at Llanberis about the year 1810, and probably the one in question.[30]

With regard to the aqueduct, it might be enquired how so costly a solution could be justified when the ample waters of Afon Nant Peris, close by, might have supplied the wheel. The answer probably lies in the fact that a vital piece of land which the leat would have crossed was held by a quarrying concern – later the Llanberis Slate Co.[31]

Ore returns credited to Llanberis from 1822 to 1840 exceeded 7000 tons sold at Swansea, of which 1169 tons – a record for a Caernarvonshire copper mine – was attributable to 1832. However by this time Llanberis, Drwyscoed and Clogwyn Coch were all managed by Joseph Jones on behalf of Thomas Assheton Smith, so it is possible that some of the Llanberis figures were augmented by Clogwyn Coch output.[32] But high returns could not compensate for low-grade ore, and in 1836 Assheton Smith leased the three mines to Richard Griffith and partners. By 1841 Llanberis

These opencuts high on the mountainside at Llanberis are probably part of the Yew Tree works.
David Bick

sales to Swansea had declined to zero, and no more were recorded until 110 tons in 1850. Too much however, ought not to be read into these official statistics for reasons explained in the introduction.

Subsequently, the mine struggled on in an intermittent and desultory fashion, but in 1870 returned 75 tons at a produce of 34% – an astonishing richness rarely, if ever, approached by any other British mine. The figure possibly refers to copper precipitate, but otherwise an ore far better than copper-pyrites is indicated. In 1873 Wallace Cragg, a director of the Glynrhonwy slate quarry, acquired a 40 year lease of the Llanberis mine and the adjacent Llanberis slate quarry, and forthwith promoted with gusto the Llanberis Copper Mining Co. Ltd., having a nominal capital of £60,000.[33] Other directors included Sir Alexander Malet K.C.B., Edwin Davis of London, and Lipscombe Seckham, Hanch Hall, Lichfield.[34]

The prospectus referred to an 8h.p. pumping and winding engine (probably a steam 'portable') and a Blake's stone-crusher at the south adit which 'at the beginning of the present century was extensively worked'.[33] There was also a 16h.p. engine at the Dol-Ithel or north adit. It appears that the stone aqueduct had been demolished, and in confirmation the photograph of the period does not show it, and neither does an 1873 plan.[31] Professor Forbes submitted a glowing report with estimated profits of £12,000 from the south level alone. Out of this promotion Cragg benefitted to the tune of £49,000 in shares and £40,000 in cash by the old trick of selling the lease to a company of his own creation.[34] He became liquidator only three years later and the concern officially dissolved in 1885 having sold no ore at all. It had no doubt ceased any activity long before. Many years previously, warnings of the pernicious effects of free share issues had been publicised but nobody, least of all promoters, took any notice.[35]

A hydro-electric storage scheme has obliterated the stamps area and the main level which, I explored in 1957. Nearly the whole length rested on timbers whilst in several

An early view of the north adit emerging under the road on the shores of Llyn Peris. The buildings probably housed the 16hp steam engine for ore-dressing machinery.
Gwynedd Archive Service

places stopes soaring quite beyond the range of carbide lamps testified to the ore removed. A fall at 193 paces prevented further progress. Two caunter-lodes had been worked, one being only a few yards inside, and there were splendid copper stains in various places.

At surface, the mountainside still reveals early adits and ore-dressing sites reminiscent of Drwsycoed. Ruins of small stone buildings, some square and some circular, dot the ground, their purpose signified by piles of handcobbed waste outside. Higher up are extensive and dangerous opencuts. Here, as at Drwsycoed, it is a pleasant task to try to correlate the evidence with the description of 1760, when hopes ran high and work had scarcely begun.

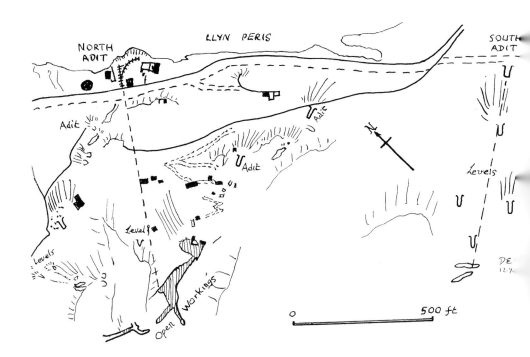

The industrial archaeology of Llanberis, based on a survey by Alasdair Neill.

8 NANT FFRANCON

In the 18th century the valley of Nant Ffrancon witnessed a number of trials for copper and other minerals, but although nothing worthwhile developed, the area is of considerable interest.

An important source of information is William Williams *Observations on the Snowdon Mountains* published in 1802. Williams was agent to the Penrhyn Estate, and from his book we learn that the Parys Mine Co. discovered 'a flattering vein of copper ore' in 1782 below Cwm Graianog, but it dwindled away after yielding only a few tons. The site no doubt corresponds to **GWAITH** (632633), of which in 1925 the Geological Survey recorded no activity for over 60 years.

The workings occurred mainly below the old road along the valley, close to tumbledown ruins that were once a home called Gwaith-maen. Quite extensive waste dumps reveal copper-pyrites, complex sulphide ores and calcite, which came from an adit under the road, now blocked. The Geological Survey mentions a shaft 9 yards deep, presumably at the same spot. Across the road is a suggestion of two grassed-over levels or trials, and a short distance up the hillside an adit has been driven 30 or 40 yards on a quartz lode.

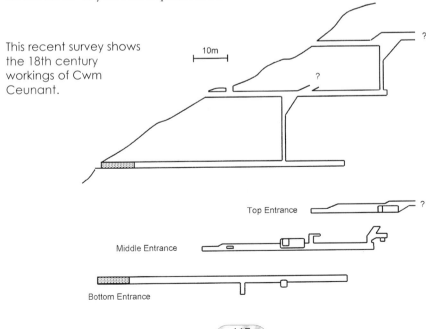

This recent survey shows the 18th century workings of Cwm Ceunant.

10m

Top Entrance

Middle Entrance

Bottom Entrance

Lower down the valley near the 1000ft contour, dumps from three workings are plainly visible at **CWM CEUNANT (626637)**. The levels are about 60ft apart vertically and the appended sketch gives an idea of the section. At the entrance to the middle level is displayed a splendid gossan lode with copper-pyrites, and on the dumps are other sulphides some of which, from their affinity for the magnet, are probably pyrrhotite. Considerable work has been done here.

To the north-east is the hitherto un-noticed mine of **CEUNANT (633645)**, the main workings being close to a sharp bend in the river. The lode can be traced by old trials southwards for over a quarter of a mile. The site must correspond to explorations made about 1760 by Archdeacon Ellis of Bangor, Mr. Hughes of Penrhyn and others 'in the hill above the farmhouse called Ceunant and also at the riverside close to that house'.[2]

In 1783 a Mr. Barker investigated various locations on the Penrhyn Estate, amongst which copper and arsenical-pyrites or mispickel were discovered above Tanygarth (638666).[3] The site yielded 232 tons of the latter mineral at a much later date, all of which was humped down the mountain by hand.[4]

Arsenic also occurred at Ceunant where it is said to have been the principal ore raised. About 1837 an English company re-opened the workings but pollution of the river and skin complaints led to a suspension of operations.[5] Whether much has been done there since is improbable.

At the site, five or six filled-in shafts close together on almost level ground follow a lode coursing a little west of south, that can be seen as a quartz rib in the river

'Cut and Cover' arsenic flues ascend this rocky outcrop at Ceunant.   *David Bick*

beyond the entrance to the adit. Nearby, a remarkable feature is a series of flues and interconnecting passages made of stone flags radiating from a common point, where there was once presumably a furnace. Each flue is about two feet square and 40 or 50ft long. They are in two groups, one being more or less horizontal whilst the other climbs a rocky knoll. The site appears to equate with a feature marked 'Works' on an 1840 plan and is of particular interest being, as far as I know, the only example in Wales of a plant designed for producing crude arsenic by calcining and sublimation.[6]

Remains of this kind encountered in Devon and Cornwall date from a much later period and probably employed somewhat different techniques. But the process was still very destructive to human life, few of the persons employed in the manufacture living beyond the age of 30 to 35 years.[7] The Ceunant site deserves a detailed study, not least since the area in 1982 was under review in connection with a projected new waterworks.

An intriguing aspect of mining history is the occasional encounter of a 'ghost' mine – that is, one for which the records appear to have no physical counterpart. In the case of **DOLAWEN**, nothing whatever has come to light. About 1760 Sir George Young, Ellis, Hughes, and Francis Lloyd a doctor from Anglesey, were involved in a copper mine 'on the slope below Cwm Dolawen', but the company being unable to agree amongst themselves the work collapsed.[5] A Cornishman named Climo later ran the mine for Sir George Young and at least one load of ore went to Macclesfield, probably to Roe & Co.[3]

In 1822 three men from Anglesey, Evan Griffith, Thomas Meyrick and Robert Griffith obtained a 21 year lease on Dolawen and Ceunant, and agreed to keep four experienced miners employed for 9 months with a very high royalty of one-fourth of dressed ore.[8] According to *The Mining Journal* between 1836 and 1839 inclusive, 128 tons of copper ore were returned at Swansea from 'Llandegai'. Unfortunately the exact origins were not quoted. Eight tons sold in April 1836 fetched the high price of £15 12s 6d. per ton.[3]

The earliest details of the workings and machinery occur in 1847 when shares in 'Dalawin' mine were offered to the public.[9] It was held under lease from Colonel Pennant who had married into the Penrhyn Estate, and there is reason to suppose that Dalawin and Dolawen were one and the same. According to the announcement, the engine-shaft had descended 30 fathoms under adit with a level driven over 30 fathoms on the course of the vein from which large quantities of copper were obtained. Above ground a 30ft diameter waterwheel with pumps, grinder, and dressing machinery had lately been erected, together with various buildings. Somewhat confusingly however, a report from George Twigge the agent, mentioned that the engine-shaft was 'only 25 yards from surface'. Whether the venture continued is not certain. Twigge came from Staffordshire and two years previously had made trials in the area of Tai-Newyddion, near Gwaith.[3]

Early in 1852, Dolawen had 47 tons of copper ore ready for sampling, the north lode looked well, and a railroad was under construction to the crushing mill. Large heaps of stuff awaited picking over, and the lode in the bottom of the 15 fathom level was 16 inches wide yielding good ore.[10] Nonetheless the plant and material came up for sale a few months later, and from the appended advertisement it is clear that much capital had been expended.[11] Of particular interest is the inclusion of what appears to be a two-stage crushing mill consisting of one pair of coarse rolls feeding two pairs of fine rolls, a kind not uncommon in the north of England at the time, but very unusual in Wales.[12] As we have seen, some of the materials went to Snowdon mine in 1852. The 5ft breast waterwheel implies a good flow of water, presumably from the Ogwen, indicating a site near the river.

From the evidence of old maps, the original dwelling of Dolawen stood near a small valley to the west of the present house of that name and was approached from the old road on the west side of the River Ogwen.[13] But within a short period, a long length of the road and buildings complete and probably the mine also, were engulfed by tips from the Penrhyn Quarries. The most likely site for the workings is about ¼ mile west of Plas Penisarnant, an area now lost beneath many feet of waste.

Another mine of doubtful whereabouts is **COED Y DINAS**, the scene of spirited trials between 1760 and 1770 for copper and lead. According to Williams a good deal of both ores were raised, but without a profit.[14] Another author, presumably referring to the same site, gives a similar account. 'About 1760 and later, attempts were made in Coed y Dinas for copper by Cornish miners, where candles were not extinguished night and day for seven years. Levels were made from the Ogwen to go under Coetmor's land. Pits were made from these, which are now full of water.... About 1802 Lord Penrhyn made attempts from the bed of the Ogwen on the same vein, going under Pen Dinas, but with little success'.[15]

A likely area for the operation is the wooded bank of the river below Coetmor Bridge (611679) where a level was reported about 1810.[16]

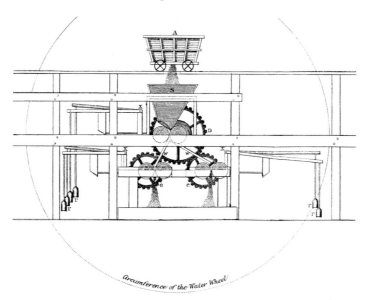

An 1821 illustration of a 3-pair roller-crusher mill as used in the north, but quite uncommon in Wales. The waterwheel scales 32 ft in diameter, and the weights hanging from the levers forced the rolls together.

'Oxydated carbonate of copper, with some specimens covered with lancet-pointed crystals of an amethystine colour' were reported at **DERWEN DEG** (762756) in 1860,[1a] and some twenty years later workings for copper went to a depth of 18 fathoms.[1b]

The mine was situated in rolling pastoral country a mile or two from Conway, on a lode running NE-SW according to the Old Series one inch geological map, and afterwards became the object of blatant promotions. The sett included parts of Panol Gwyn, Derwen Deg, Gwern Fechana, Hafoty Bach and Tanybwlch; £40,000 was asked, which the agent considered cheap at the price.[2]

The Derwen Deg and Panol Gwyn Copper & Lead Mining Company was registered in March 1878, the subscribers nearly all having Liverpool addresses; in July 1881 the North Wales Freehold Copper Mines and Smelting Co. took control with a nominal capital of £250,000. Although the sett now aggregated merely 20 acres, the purchase price amounted to no less than £100,000, a figure which was considered justified, or at least rendered somewhat less implausible, by a very favourable inspection carried out in the name of the Geological Survey by its director, Professor A.C. Ramsay.

A full-page advertisement followed, revealing the directors as General Downing of Sevenoaks, H.H. Fanshawe of the Carlton Club, Sir Henry Gould of Croydon, and R.M. Fabris and Henry Gielgud, both of London. An accompanying text in the best promotional style implied the existence of a lode 6ft wide in solid copper ore, which a little later was said to run 33oz/ton of silver. As if this were insufficient inducement a newly discovered champion lode was mentioned, with samples 'of the richest and most extraordinary descriptions ever beheld'. Also published was a fanciful plan of the sett marking various features and a veritable spider's web of copper and lead lodes amounting to eleven in number – a caricature which nevertheless has somehow found its way into the archives.[3] (see next page)

Such extravagant claims did not go unnoticed. In August 1881, D.C. Davies commented upon the absurdity of the purchase price, and concluded by expressing regret that 'one who bears a high and honoured place in science' had become associated with the venture.

In October the mine agent Capt. H.B. Vercoe reported the arrival of a new 24-inch crushing machine from Conway. This was soon followed by negotiations with the London & North Western Railway for special rates for conveyance of ore to Vivians of Swansea, not that more than a load or two had yet materialised.

Plant included four 14hp pumping and winding engines, two 10hp portables, a

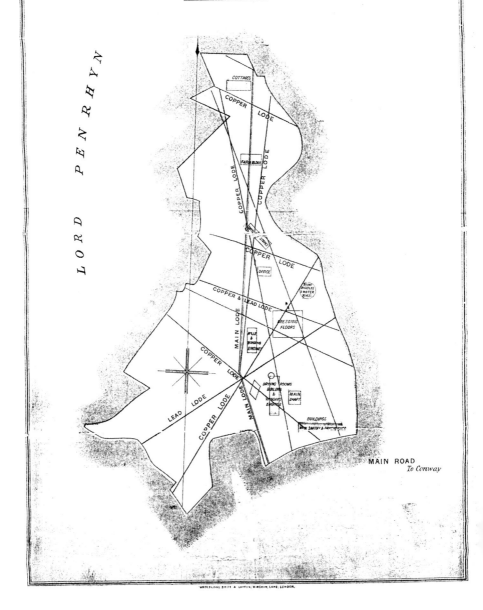

The North Wales Freehold Copper Mines and Smelting Company, Limited.

PLAN OF MINING SETT.
(SHEWING RUN & POSITION OF LODES)

waterwheel and buddles, jiggers and rockbreakers. A viaduct carried a tramroad to the mill, and the buildings comprised the agent's residence, crusher-house, blacksmiths' and carpenters' shops, a smithy with two forges and a weighbridge.

By the spring of 1882 prospects appeared less auspicious; $9^1/_2$ inch pumps had to be installed whilst sinking for a new level, water rather than copper increasing as the mine deepened. The end was not long delayed, and the company went into liquidation only nine months after formation. Perhaps Vercoe was unaware of the situation, but certainly very few were taken in by his futile comment a week or two later – 'at no time since the company took over have the mines looked as well as now'.

Surprisingly, both Vercoe and Derwen Deg survived, for a revival took place in 1882 as the Conway Valley Freehold Mining Co. Soon afterwards, the supporting walls of the pumping angle-bob failed, requiring a rebuild, and extensive flooding resulted underground in the meantime. But reports continued enthusiastically; 'one of the most magnificent sights I have seen for many years – large boulders of beautifully crystallized quartz, thickly studded with cubes of rich peacock copper ore – I never saw a finer lode'. Since however iron-pyrites not copper-pyrites crystallises in cubes, the fate of this promotion followed a predictable course, and nothing more was heard beyond a mention of driving a 42 fathom level north in August 1883.

A century later a house and landscaped gardens occupy the site of Derwen Deg and nothing remains of this remarkable bubble mine beyond a level, the semblance of a shaft and a large quarry-like excavation in private woodland at the rear.[4] There is however, half a mile to the north near a cattle grid on the roadside, an exposure of mineralized ground in a rock face, including iron-staining and nicely crystallised quartz.

In journeying northwards to the copper deposits of the Great Orme, the opportunity cannot be missed to mention a unique and little-known occurrence of considerable scientific interest within a stone's throw of the route, at **BWLCH** (787794) near Deganwy. Unfortunately little of its history has so far come to light.

On a hillside, the workings exploited an east-west lode in opthitic dolerite by adits and at least one shaft, said to be 120 ft deep, and constituted the only antimony mine in Wales. According to the late Sir Arthur Russell, the vein comprised quartz and chert with sundry metallic minerals including stibnite and semseyite, a sulphide of lead and antimony for which Glendenning in Scotland is the only other British locality.[5] A clue to the date of working is the inscription 'Mine of Antimony' on a map of 1837.[6] Four men were employed here in 1896, when the owner was listed as Thomas Barker. In recent years a bulldozer has largely put paid to the site, although the remnants of a dump may still reward the minerologist's attention.

Carboniferous Limestone forms the domelike peninsula of the Great Orme, where it included several very productive copper lodes with, in addition, ores running along the beds of strata. The minerals were mainly malachite and copper pyrites, the latter predominating in depth. The mines have been described in detail by C J Williams, and the following is largely based on his account.[7]

Ancient workings have long been known here, and their great age and extent were confirmed by the pioneer work of Duncan James in the 1970s. The Great Orme Exploration Society carried on the research in 1987/8, and soon revealed a vast warren of stopes and galleries to a depth of over 200ft and covering some six acres at surface. These subterranean workings were the biggest of their kind yet discovered in Europe. Carbon 14 dating imputed an activity extending well over a millenium, roughly between 1,900 and 600 BC, and the Gwynedd Archaeological Trust added further evidence as to the age and development of the mine.[8] Some of the workings were very small, scarcely large enough for a child, and many had been backfilled by waste from more modern operations. The underground passages extended over three miles and a profusion of stone hammers, and bone and wooden tools confirmed their antiquity.

Much of the ground was a decomposed dolomitic limestone interspersed with copper minerals and relatively easy to excavate. The quantity removed has been calculated to exceed 50,000 cubic yards or some 100,000 tons, but this of course would far exceed the actual tonnage of dressed or concentrated ore obtained. Very little mineral now remains to be seen to give an indication of the original orebody, and estimating the output is like asking a stranger to assess what has gone from a burgled house. Five or ten thousand tons might be a reasonable guess, but spread over a dozen centuries the figure is much less impressive, perhaps averaging five tons of concentrated ore every year or 2cwt per week. In short, the picture rather suggests that the operations were on quite a small scale, and only employing a handful of people at a time. The riddle of the ultimate fate of the ores, how much for smelting to metal and how much for other purposes, will never be known, but some observations on the question in general have been made in Chapter One.

These discoveries led to the formation of the Great Orme Mine Co in 1990, and construction of a visitor centre including general information and displays of finds. This has become a major tourist attraction, not least with the ancient surface workings exposed and underground trips giving a fascinating insight into conditions thousands of years ago.

The **LLANDUDNO OLD MINE** (771831) on land belonging to the Bishop of Bangor and the **NEW MINE** on the Mostyn Estate were situated close together near the top of the Orme, on a group of parallel lodes ranging northwards from the coast at Penmorfa to St. Tudno's Church. Workings were drowned out before 1748, but after 1761 operations continued more or less without intermission for many years under various managements.

In 1824 Samuel Worthington of Llandegai took over the workings. The lease covered some 700 acres and was renewed in 1837 for the lives of his sons Archibald and William. Some of the produce went to Amlwch for smelting with inferior grades of Anglesey ore, a practice which continued at all three Llandudno mines until closure.

The New Mine was mainly on Mostyn land at Pyllau, just to the west of Old Mine. Both workings laboured under heavy pumping costs, and when the New Mine became drowned out the two ventures banded together in driving a sea-level adit half a mile in length. Work began at Penmorfa in 1834 under the direction of Captain Davey of the Old Mine and Thomas Jones, agent to the New Mine, and the level holed through into the flooded workings in October 1842, some 400 feet below surface. Rails were laid down to enable ore to be trammed out and dressed near the entrance.

Previously there had been a valiant attempt to pump the Old Mine by a long line of brammock-rods or flat-rods extending over the Great Orme from Gogarth near the western shore.[9] A small spring of water high on the hillside provided the motive power by means of a 'Tom and Jerry' or flopjack engine consisting of a large tank on a hinged frame receiving the flow. A valve automatically discharged the contents at the lowest point of travel, the tank then returning to its upper attitude, the whole arc of movement being perhaps seven or eight feet.

In the form of a huge chain of wood and iron, the brammock-rods were connected to the frame and maintained in tension by the weight of the pump-work in the shaft. They would thus transmit motion in a reciprocating fashion to the mine out of sight over the hill, the cycling rate probably being as low as once every five or ten minutes. The installation was attributed to Thomas Jones.

Power transmission by these primitive mechanical contrivances was common in mining districts for distances sometimes exceeding a mile, though in this instance it has to be doubted whether the application proved successful, not so much due to the means, but because of the source of power itself. Flop-jack engines could only produce a useful power on a copious supply of water. In addition, unlike water-pressure engines which were virtually steam-engines running on water, they could not take advantage of a high head, although this was available at Gogarth. Thus it can be seen that flop-jacks were unsuited to the site, and eventually there followed the logical step of substituting a water-pressure engine.

In 1835, probably to counter deficiencies in the flop-jack, an 18 inch steam-engine by Sandys, Carne & Vivian of Cornwall was erected near Vivian's Shaft. The Old

Felicia Simpson's watercolour of 1853 shows the enginehouse near Vivians Shaft and the brammock-rods striding over the Orme to Gogarth.   *David Bick*

Mine passed into the hands of John Hughes in 1846 and a contemporary report gives valuable details of the plant. By this time the engine's duties were referred to as driving 'an ore-crusher on its east side, and a winding apparatus on the west side adapted for two shafts'. Surprisingly, there was now no mention of pumping, although

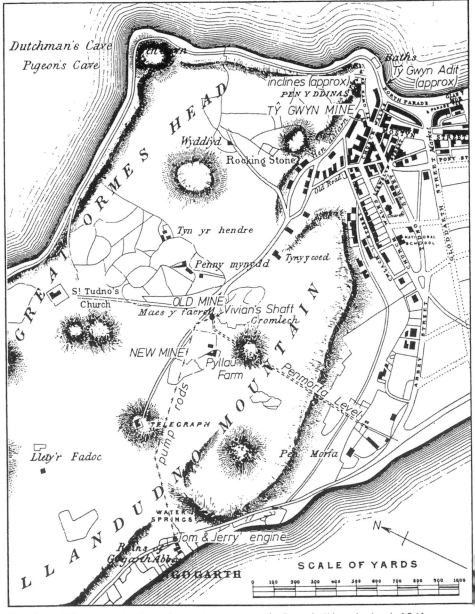

The Great Orme and mines, based on a map in Parry's 'Llandudno', 1861.

C J Williams

according to the report the brammock-rods from Gogarth still ended at the engine – a statement confirmed by the 1847 enclosure award map, via Higher Shaft. Perhaps the steam-engine could be coupled to assist the water-pressure engine at times of peak demand – a very unusual arrangement, or else the rods were disconnected at the pump end.

The water-pressure engine must have proved successful, for another was proposed in 1848 for fitting underground to pump 65 yards below deep adit, the estimated cost of £140 to be borne jointly by the two companies. A $6^1/_2$ inch diameter piston with a 66 yard head of water was considered sufficient to operate 3 inch pumps at least, the chosen site being in the New Mine adjoining Pyllau. Whether the plans came to fruition is not certain.

The Old Mine made £7,400 profit between 1825 and 1844, but by 1846 was losing money. The company had however, received substantial sums from royalties from 25 acres leased to the Ty Gwyn mine at the east end of the Orme. In November 1849 a vast underground reservoir or cavern was encountered, from which water issued at the rate of 10,000 gallons per minute, putting paid to all work below adit for a number of years.

John Hughes died in 1850 and a new company called the Llandudno Mine took over in 1853. The management was entrusted to the mining engineers John Taylor & Sons, William Vivian acting as captain. The mine now presented a sorry spectacle being 'entirely out of working order', and profits remained elusive in spite of a substantial output of ore following the injection of much capital.

The lease passed to David Lloyd of Llandudno in 1861 but results did not improve and twenty years later the adventurers finally gave in. Nevertheless the record was an honourable one, some £200,000 worth of ore according to estimate having been raised even before 1845.

The ore was generally rich, in the upper levels some proportion being malachite or copper carbonate – a mineral practically unknown in economic quantities elsewhere in Wales. Native copper also occurred.[10] At both mines the lodes were largely confined to certain beds of crystalline limestone and died out when traversing other beds. But regardless of the nature of the host rock, large deposits of ore were encountered at the intersection of cross-veins or caunter lodes, as is often the case.[11]

At the Old Mine at surface were warehouses, miners' cabins, a counting-house, smithy, brass foundry, assay office and carpenters shop, not to mention horse-whims and the steam engine, little or nothing of which now remains. North of Pyllau the ground is pock-marked with trials extending over the saddle of the Orme, and Vivian's Shaft is part of the visitor centre.

A very interesting feature is the course of the brammock-rods from Higher Shaft, which is identified by a long row of oval pits a few feet deep and 20 or 30 feet apart, some being lined with masonry. These pits presumably housed struts that swung like inverted pendulums to support the rods. For some inexplicable reason their presence is only apparent towards the ends of the run, the nearly level portion across the saddle of the hill being, as far as I can see, devoid of any signs at all.

The little spring of clear water still flows, and the brammock-rod pits cease at the edge of a steep escarpment, below which was the Gogarth water-pressure engine, fed

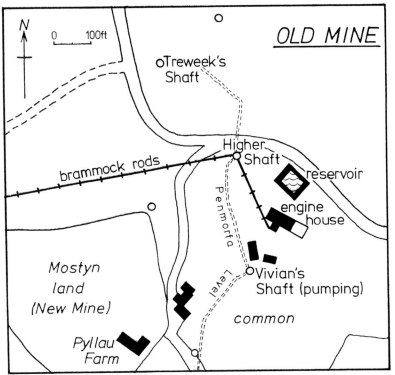

Llandudno Old Mine, based on the enclosure map, 1847.
C J Williams

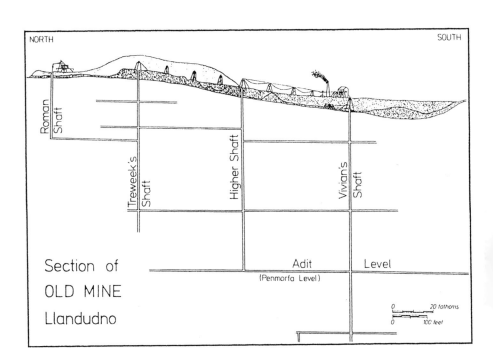

by pipes capable of withstanding some 100 lbs per square inch hydraulic pressure. The rods did not take a direct course over the hill, but deviated slightly at a point SSW of the summit café. From Ordnance maps, the length measures about 1000 yards, so that the 1300 yard figure mentioned in the 1846 report is difficult to reconcile. At all events, the run is comparable with similar flat-rod installations worked by waterwheels in mid-Wales at Esgair-hir and Darren, and in surveying this windswept hillside we can only applaud the 19th century engineers who risked their reputations on contrivances of this kind. In the words of Dr. Samuel Johnson concerning a dog walking upon its hind legs – 'It is not done well; but you are surprised to find it done at all'.

At the eastern end of the Great Orme, **TY GWYN** (778828) worked a copper deposit running north of west and reputedly discovered by a clod of earth thrown up by a cow. Nothing has come to light as to its early years, but from letters to *The Mining Journal*, we learn that the mine had huge potential from the beginning. It started on a capital of only £600 in 1827 if not before, and for a time did very well. There was apparently no fissure lode as such, but beds or 'flats' up to 10 or 20ft thick outcropping more or less from the seashore and containing malachite, grey and blue ores yielding up to 40% copper. These were due to secondary enrichment, and gave way to copper pyrites at 10 to 20% metal in depth. By 1847, ores worth over £90,000 had been raised, but after the initial success, problems with water were such that the income never exceeded the cost. One commentator expressed much sympathy with the adventurers who, in spite of all their spirit and perseverance had ended up badly the loser, yet by the terms of the lease had handed over to the landowner one-sixth part of their total returns, amounting to upwards of £15,000. Once again, even with

On the top of The Great Orme, these pits mark the course of the Brammock-rods between Gogarth and the Old Mine. *Wendy Foulkes*

Felicia Simpson's impression of Tynfron in 1853 shows the tall Sims enginehouse, shear-legs and boilerhouse, all going to ruin. Soon afterwards the site was submerged into Llandudno.

David Bick

a mine so rich as Ty Gwyn, a royalty based on sales regardless of profit or loss had shown how iniquitous the system could be.

Initally, the mine was worked behind Belmont from two inclined drifts at about 1 in 4 which followed the orebody down, but at 125 fathoms salt water broke in, and was excluded only with great difficulty. It returned in torrents later. A new company was formed in 1835 and installed a 50 inch engine from the Halkin lead mines, but it was never adequate for the task. In 1842, major shareholders were William Jones of Bodhyfryd, Llandudno, and Mrs. Ann Douglas of Cheltenham, but by then the mine was in debt, with no funds to pay the men.[12]

A further pumping engine became essential, and £7,812 was raised with difficulty for this and other purposes, tenders being invited in March 1842 for building the enginehouse.[13] Unfortunately, the choice of engine fell upon an unproven design of James Sims, a Cornish engineer, which consisted of compounded cylinders in tandem, one above the other, arranged vertically in the usual configuration for beam-engines.[14] However worthy the system may have appeared theoretically, in practice serious drawbacks arose, not least the cost and the difficulty of easy access to the lower cylinder and stuffing-box. There is little doubt that the decision contributed to the early demise of the venture.

By May 1843 debts amounted to nearly £4,000, and in addition one of the three boilers for the new engine (a 50 inch + 90 inch) fell out of repair. Worse followed in

July, and with the engine 'out of order and one of the cylinders much damaged' the workings inevitably flooded, bringing activity to a stand.

After a chancery suit in 1846 and with a revised management, the mine reopened under the Tynfron. The enterprise consisted of sinking a new shaft on higher ground to gain the orebody beyond the flooded workings, but the object was only partly achieved, if at all. Exactly where ore was raised at this time is unclear, but once again water broke in with such vigour that the miners were forced to leave their drills abandoned in the lode. This was the end of Ty Gwyn, and the machinery came up for auction in July 1856. It included both engines, an 18in crushing mill and a 'portable' 22in pumping and winding engine which had perhaps been used at Tynfron shaft, just east of Wyddfyd Road. The fate of the big Sims engine is unknown; it was probably converted to simple working or broken up on the spot.

As to the archaeology of the mine, in recent years the Great Orme Exploration Society has gained access via a manhole into an adit which ran straight for 495yd to Tynfron shaft, now capped. The level cuts through the original adit which began near the site of the Grand Hotel and intersected the Ty Gwyn pumping shaft, within the hairpin bend in Ty Gwyn Road. Such are the remnants of one of the richest copper mines ever worked in Wales. But like so many ventures it promised much yet, for all the best endeavours, never to yielded the blessed fruit of success.

This rotative beam engine from Ty Gwyn was used at collieries in the Wrexham district before being scrapped in 1921.   *Gwynedd Archive Service*

10 FFESTINIOG

This chapter covers a number of minor workings well off the beaten track, but nevertheless worthy of mention. The first, **MOEL FLEIDIAU** or **CWMFYNHADOG** (675493), lies about three miles north-west of Blaenau Ffestiniog near of the source of Afon Lledr, being marked as 'copper mine' on the Old Series one-inch Ordnance map. In 1838, seven men were 'working a lead ore level' under Jones & Co. The last activity was in 1871.[1] The following notes are based on observations made during the autumn of 1953.

The vein strikes a little south of west alongside the infant river, and for some distance its outcrop forms the bed of the stream. At the lower or eastern end, an adit was driven west along the lode which is revealed about 15ft wide in two opencuts. The first of these displayed a rib of galena and permitted access to the adit and a winze below. In the forebreast of the level some 10 yards to the west were vughs or cavities lined with crystalline quartz and copper-pyrites.

In this vicinity rock outcrops flank the lode, and the whole rears like a whale above the surrounding landscape. Into the ridge had been driven two crosscut adits, grassgrown, and probably antedating the above workings. Beyond, where the lode outcrops in or adjacent to the stream, sulphides of iron, zinc, copper and arsenic were visible together with gossan up to 6ft in width. The site is a first-rate example of a mineral lode exposed at surface and well rewards a walk over the hills.

The Old Series geological map reveals a complex network of faults in the desolate mountains north and east of Ffestiniog, an area riddled with slate workings, one of which is said to form a bunker for Royalty, V.I.P.s and art treasures in event of a nuclear war – the modern equivalent of Egyptian kings entombed with goods and chattels for use in a life hereafter.

Several faults carry sufficient copper and lead to be designated mineral lodes and have encouraged a number of trials. One such lode south of Llyn Bowydd strikes east-west at **NEWBOROUGH** or **OFFEREN** (730465) and reveals much zinc-blende with patches of copper-pyrites and cubes of galena. There are also minor amounts of pyrites with traces of bornite and covellite.[2]

In 1850 shares came on the market 'in the well known and valuable lead works called the Newborough Mine' and a few years afterwards gold was reported there.[3] After a long interlude, John L.M. Frazer late of the Minera mines, floated the British Silver-Lead Mining Co. Ltd. in July 1878 to purchase the sett from David Roberts, who held it under a grant from Lord Newborough. The deepest shaft did not exceed 5 fathoms, where according to Henry Francis of Llanidloes, the lode revealed

The lode at Newborough is exposed in the open-workings.
John Burman

'carbonate of lime, quartz, blende, copper and rich silver-lead ore'.[4a] But metal prices at this time had fallen badly and in spite of a favourable report from Captain Walter Eddy in September 1881, little or nothing resulted. Nevertheless Frazer persevered undauntedly, as late as the autumn of 1887 still sending in glowing reports of prospects to *The Mining Journal*.

Lack of waterpower handicapped development, though the Ffestiniog railway extension to Rhiwbach quarries running within a stone's throw provided a useful asset. Today, waste heaps white with quartz and a water-filled shaft with the lode exposed in a rocky outcrop mark the site, together with two iron plates about 5ft x 1ft x 1½ inches, which perhaps served as anvils for manual ore-crushing. A preponderance of blende no doubt indicates that it would not bear the cost of carriage, the railway notwithstanding.

In 1834 a lead mine was recorded at 'Gam-allt', a couple of miles to the south[4b], where two quite extensive trials on different properties have given rise to some confusion of identity. The larger may be termed **AFON GAMALLT** (733434) and consists of workings on a lode running alongside the stream. According to the Geological Survey, the lode is up to 6ft wide of brecciated ashes and volcanic agglomerates cemented by quartz. The mineral ores are galena, blende, copper and iron-pyrites with some malachite and azurite, and up to 17 dwt of gold per ton of copper-pyrites.[5]

The workings include opencuts and trenches now largely grassed over and at the eastern end is a fine semi-circular masonry portal to a cross-cut level. An adit at the western end extends about 40 yards on the lode and at the forebreast reveals copper stains and a four-inch clay leader; the entrance is nearly blocked. Traces of a leat can be distinguished, and a cart-track leads to the mine from the south, passing the old Drum slate-quarry and incline, abandoned about 1880.

The Geological Survey description concludes with a mention of a lead lode rendered unworkable due to problems of access at **LLYNAU GAMALLT** (743443). The course of the main fault is identified from a distance by a great wall of rock silhouetted in the morning light, where two lodes also yielding gold have been traced by sundry scratchings and a crosscut adit. The Roman Road of Sarn Helen bounds the sett on one side, which according to Ordnance maps now belongs to the National Trust.

In 1890 the sett formed the object of a promotion by the Gamallt Co. Ltd., which had secured a lease from Randall Casson of Porthmadog. In November 1889, Captain Matthew Francis of Flintshire reported upon the prospects to the promoters, Messrs Montague Higginson & Arthur Thompson of Liverpool. He referred to assays for gold yielding up to nearly 2oz per ton of quartz and concluded that he 'had never seen a lead mining grant which with the development so limited, bristled with so many indications of success'. A more cautious report by Alfred Harper Curtis of the firm Bewick & Moering, London, raised the possibility of a tramroad to the G.W.R., a distance of three miles, but did not consider it justified unless the slate deposits on the sett were also exploited. Curtis described the main lode as having Llandeilo Slate on the one side and eruptive felstone on the other, with a 'horse' of felsite rock separating it from a parallel loop vein which appeared to merge at each end. The horse was up to 76ft wide and about 3/8th mile in length. Both lodes contained lead at surface, particularly the main lode where rich ore was being blasted during the inspection. The cross-cut adit revealed mineralization but had not reached the footwall of the main lode, far less the parallel lode.[6a]

Curtis stated that most of the work was of recent origin, but some of the trials were grassgrown (and thus at such an altitude, of considerable antiquity). As to the auriferous quartz, reservations were expressed as to the quantity available. A copper lode near the Roman ford was also mentioned, upon which old workers had driven a short adit (729433). A preliminary prospectus issued in May 1890 quoted only favourable extracts from both reports, but in spite of this precaution little resulted beyond the employment of two or three men at surface until 1892.

South of the Bala-Ffestiniog road is **CWM CYNFAL** (737416), perched above a deep and inaccessible ravine. The lode outcrops between the road and Afon Cynfal, and strikes somewhat parallel to both, extending over a mile. Samuel Lewis referred to a copper mine at 'Cwm Cynfael' and a few years later, in 1839, Mangnel & Co. were working a copper mine near Ffestiniog; it was probably the same.[6b] In 1888 John Robertson & Partners of Sunderland were listed as owners, and under the Cynfal Mining Co., eight or ten men worked below ground for several years without however, any production appearing in official statistics.

As far as could be ascertained in October 1953 only one of several adits remained open, the portal being directly above the gorge. The level extended 40 or 50 yards north-west to the lode and about 10 yards beyond, of which the latter distance was in very soft shale. A short drivage had been made on the lode, terminating at the east end in a blocked-up rise. The vein included a wide rib of quartz with a little copper, worsening towards the west. At the intersection with the adit was a filled-in winze, also a rise leading to several higher levels and a further rise that must have extended practically to grass. Waste had been tipped into the ravine.

Small dumps displayed copper minerals at the outcrop and to the west, two very

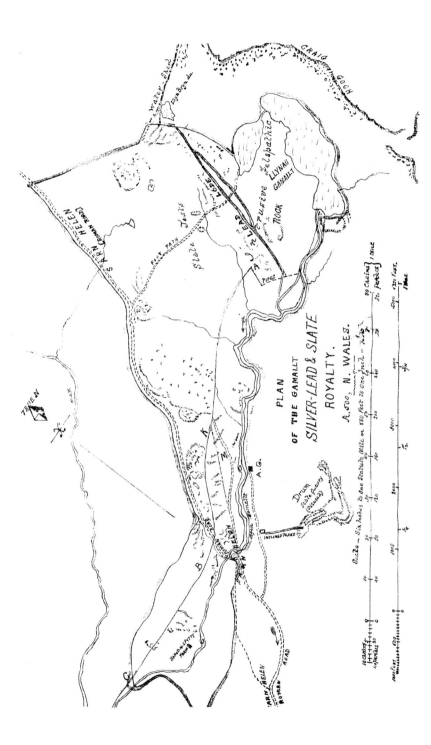

This promotional plan of the Llynau Gamallt sell shows the 'Lead Lode' and the Roman Road of Sarn Helen. South of the stream were the Afon Gamallt workings and the abandoned Drum slate quarry.

Clwyd RO

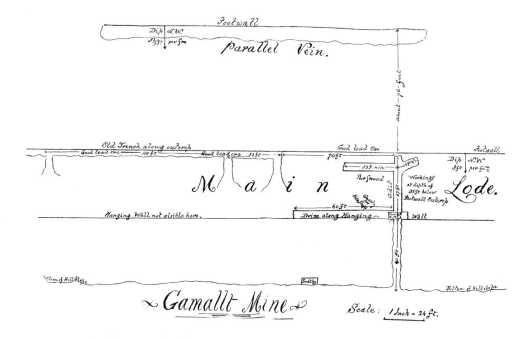

A plan showing trial workings on the main lode at Llynau Gamallt.   *Clwyd R O*

old blocked-up levels could be observed by the side of a stream. The Geological Survey refers to a big pocket of copper ore worked at Cwm Cynfal, but nothing has been found to confirm this.[7]

Across the mining area east of Ffestiniog, Sarn Helen follows a very tortuous route, which was perhaps an earlier British trackway adapted by the Romans, at least in this vicinity. The road also traverses the gold district of the Mawddach valley, the silver-lead district of Llanfair Clydogau, and the Roman gold mines of Pumpsaint, so that there may be an association with the occurrence of precious metals. It might of course, be nothing more than coincidence, but that is the stuff of history.

11 D.C. DAVIES, F.G.S.[1]

Although well known in his day as a mining engineer and geologist of the first integrity, the name of David Christopher Davies has long been forgotten except as author of several books on mining and quarrying, which are now collector's items.

Davies was born on 13th September 1827 in humble and obscure circumstances, but in true Samuel Smiles 'self-help' tradition rose to make his mark. Orphaned at an early age, before 12 years old he became apprenticed to a Mr. Minchall, ironmonger of Oswestry, and appears eventually to have acquired the business, being described in 1856 as 'tinman and brazier' of Leg Street. He later moved to Salop Road.[2]

Since childhood, Davies pursued the study of geology and mining with almost obsessive enthusiasm, often rising at 4am, and became expert in his locality, contributing papers at least as early as 1858. A life-long friend was William Whitwell F.G.S. (1839-1920), an Inland Revenue Officer with a keen interest in botany and geology. Whitwell's job involved several moves and after he left the district the two men corresponded for many years. Both held strong religious beliefs, and Davies' faith, though not entirely free from doubt, was sufficient to permit a jest at its expense. 'I have just returned from the union meeting completely charged with Congregational Electricity. It comes click click from my tongue and streams out at my fingers ends....'

He was a compulsive lay preacher. 'No sermons ever grew more out of a man's experience than these have done out of mine', he wrote. He devoted his first book *The Christ for all the Ages* to a collection of these and produced it by raising money by subscription; a printer's error in the proofs had an amusing consequence when 'travels through space to the Heavenly Jerusalem' appeared as 'travels through Spain'. 200 subscribers sufficed to cover the cost, and Hodder and Stoughton undertook the distribution.

Davies had five children – Christopher, Edward Henry (born 1856), Polly, Nellie and Lizzie, of whom the latter died in 1871 after a long illness. The family visited Borth in 1865 and through the influence of a local magistrate he visited Clogau gold mine, then hard at work.

Whitwell's letters to Davies sometimes ran to over 50 pages. Whitwell, a batchelor, had time for such excesses and once or twice Davies attempted matchmaking; 'Mrs. Moss is a very nice ladylike young widow *indeed,* and supposing you were in search of a wife and did not mind three little children to begin with, she would be the very one to make you happy..'

Davies contributed a large number of papers to learned societies and periodicals, amongst which may be mentioned the British Architect, British Quarterly, Colliery

Guardian, Iron, Liverpool Geological Society, Powysland Club, Geological Association, Geological Magazine, and the Geological Society, to which he became formally admitted in 1872.

Such activities brought introductions to many prominent geologists including Etheridge, Morris, Jukes, Prestwich, Ramsay and William Phillips, whom he greatly admired. He thought Ramsay overbearing. Such homely titles as *The Youths Playhour and Boys Journal* were not beneath his notice, and Davies described in its pages how he first became interested in geology, with hints for beginners and offers of help in case any problems arose.

In August 1870 he escorted Professors Morris of London University and Tennant of Kings College during a week in the Oswestry district.

'On Friday the shops were closed for the Institute Fete so in a carriage and pair we started from the Wynnstay Arms for Penygarnedd to see the Phosphate beds. We put up at the little public house where you and I once had some bread and cheese and ale and a very pleasant day we had though it was frightfully hot as we walked up the hill. I learned some new facts and got hold of some new principles from Professor Morris . . . a charming week full of healthy pleasurable intellectual excitement. Professor Morris seems by far the best out-door geologist. He expressed himself very much pleased with my papers . . . and urged me to complete them and publish them.....'

Ebnal Lodge, the home of the Davies family after 1874.   *David Bick*

The idea appealed, and Davies thereupon began work on *The Geology of the North Wales Border*, to represent the sum of his labours in the region. The Powysland Club offered to publish, but for some unaccountable reason he declined, again preferring the tedious and uncertain method of subscription. A quarto volume was envisaged, selling at two guineas – a figure indicating a very substantial work.

Later in 1870, Davies led the British Association to the Llangollen area and recorded a ride up an incline to Mr. Isaac Williams' limestone quarries. At this time Christopher became engaged to a local girl with strong tee-total principles and the improbable name of Polly Walley; Davies did not conceal his relief when his son eventually married another. Christopher worked in a solicitor's practice in Newcastle and became an author in the field of rural adventure and natural history.[3]

It was the younger son, Edward Henry, who followed his father's footsteps, and Davies' gradual conversion to geology and mining as professions was no doubt encouraged by the boy's interest, as well as to establish his future. Due to a decline in trade after the railway boom, the ironmonger's shop provided a bare living and Davies was constantly in debt to Whitwell, who appears as a generous and forebearing friend. To save a workman's wages, a bench fitted in the kitchen enabled him simultaneously to work and mind the shop.

Davies had drawn attention to extensive beds of phosphate ores accompanying the Bala Limestone, and this led to the task of opening up deposits in the Berwyns above Llangynog for Hills of Deptford. Commencing in 1872 the venture lasted a number of years but eventually failed due to transport costs and falling prices.[4] He was also acquainted with S.R. Pattison F.G.S. (1809-1901), author of *Religious Life in England* and a number of mining and geological papers, and in July 1872 examined a quarry in the Lingula Flags under Cader Idris on his instructions. There were now hopes of relinquishing the shop, and a pious acquaintance observed 'you are getting very worldly going after mines and them things'.

In 1872 he became closely involved in several coal mining enterprises near home, and was soon appointed manager of the Ifton Colliery, east of Chirk. A scheme for a new coalfield south of the Mendips beneath the Oolite and New Red also demanded attention, and early in 1874 on the strength of the new position at Ifton the much awaited release came when a Mr. Lacon took over the ironmonger's shop. The family moved nearer the colliery to Ebnal Lodge, a rented farm where agriculture brought in a little extra money.

In the spring of 1875 Davies examined various properties between Darlington and Goole, followed by a colliery expedition to South Wales. In the autumn he was reporting on slate quarries in North Wales, and met Professor Etheridge. The phosphate deposits of Llanerfel near Bala required a long journey once a week early in 1876, but all the while the principal effort went into a new sinking at Ifton, known as No.3 pit or Ifton Rhyn, some 400 yards west of the old workings. This was the great hope for Henry's future as well as his own, and the collapse of the venture shortly afterwards 'solely for the want of sufficient capital', proved a sore disappointment.[5]

The prospectus for *The Geology of the North Wales Border*, still uncompleted, did not appear till September 1876. By the following February Davies had obtained 138

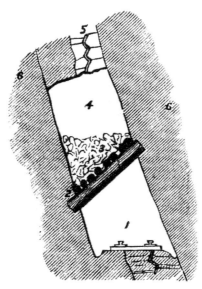

FIG. 124.—TIMBERING OF LEVEL
IN NARROW WORKINGS.

FIG. 125.—TIMBERING OF LEVEL IN
WIDE WORKINGS.

Roadway. 2, Roof timbers. 3, Rubbish. 4. Working space. 5. Lode. 6, Strata
a part of which by the side of the lode has to be taken down, and forms rubbish, 3.

An illustration by Henry Davies for his father's book
'Metalliferous Minerals and Mining'.

subscribers but a year later, still feeling unable to proceed, he expressed a fear which haunts many an author, that the fruits of his labour may never see the light of day. In allusion, when replying to Whitwell's letter received on his 50th birthday, he wrote 'I trust my life and powers may be spared so that I may accomplish the work on which my heart is set . . . but I cannot hide from myself that my best and most

D C Davies's last letter to William Whitwell. The black border denoted a period of mourning after his wife's death.

A TREATISE ON

EARTHY AND OTHER MINERALS

AND MINING

BY

D. C. DAVIES, M.E., F.G.S.

AUTHOR OF 'A TREATISE ON METALLIFEROUS MINERALS AND MINING,' 'SLATE AND
SLATE QUARRYING,' ETC.

Third Edition, Thoroughly Revised and Enlarged

BY HIS SON

E. HENRY DAVIES, M.E., F.G.S.

WITH ABOUT ONE HUNDRED ILLUSTRATIONS

LONDON

CROSBY LOCKWOOD & SON

7, STATIONERS' HALL COURT, LUDGATE HILL

1892

The title page of the third edition of Davies's *Earthy and Other Minerals and Mining,* 1892. His books are now collectors' items and very scarce.

vigorous work lies in the past'. Everyday pressures and constant travelling were other factors, and in addition his *Slate and Slate Quarrying* was in the press.

In the summer of 1878 he recorded 'I propose shortly to issue a circular explaining the delay in the large book and to make an effort to get 40 additional subscribers without which I do not think I should be justified in publishing'. Davies was also busy preparing his Manual of Metalliferous Mines & Mining. 'It is growing into an important book and will I think prove a very useful one'. Published in 1881 under the title *Metallferous Minerals & Mining* and illustrated by Henry, it ran to a number of editions and received widespread acclaim; the slate volume was also re-printed, one edition being in Welsh. How these titles came about is uncertain, but royalties and publicity for his career no doubt provided a spur.

In October 1878 father and son superintended new slate quarries at Llanglydwen in Carmarthenshire, and a series of commissions abroad were now on the horizon. He recorded in October 1880 'I have worked very hard this last three years and I have travelled very much . . . I have become connected with some very valuable deposits of copper and lead with a large proportion of silver in Norway and Sweden and it's probable that we shall have occasion to go out there frequently....' Preaching continued at Preeshenlle near Ebnal Lodge, but from this period his letters to Whitwell became much less frequent.

Davies carried off several Eisteddfod prizes for geological essays, including one of 30 guineas at Caernarvon in 1880 for *The Metalliferous Deposits of Denbighshire & Flintshire*, and about this time opened quarries in France and Germany. He was also North Wales Correspondent of *The Mining Journal* and in 1881 had a good deal of work in Cardiganshire including the mill at Bryndyfi, an abortive lead mine near Borth.[6]

In the autumn, he expressed the hope of accomplishing two more books, *Earthy and Other Minerals and Mining,* and *The Geology of the North Wales Border.* But the observation cannot be concealed that in respect of the latter, other titles were constantly taking precedence, and furthermore, he was himself undermining its potential by continuing to publish geological papers on the region.[7] Perhaps he had come to doubt his ability fully to meet the challenge of a major work, but whatever the reason the refusal of the Powysland Club's offer proved fatal, and the final steps were never taken.

After a long period of ill-health Mrs. Davies died in 1883, a year in which he made several trips abroad, including Spain and Norway. The family had now dispersed except perhaps for Polly; Henry to the South of France, and Nelly to become the wife of R.A. Richards of the chemical works, Maesbury.[8] Davies seemed well, but confessed to loneliness. The wheel had almost turned a circle, and he died of a heart attack whilst returning on the S.S. Angelo from Christiansund in September 1885. Though scarcely beyond middle age he had accomplished an astonishing amount, hardly relaxing for an instant, and the effort had taken its toll.

D.C. Davies' extensive geological collection found its way into Oswestry library, which as a Town Councillor in 1870 he had spent much time and trouble promoting. I do not know if the man is still remembered in his native town, but the collection disappeared many years ago when interest in such things had fallen to a low ebb, and like his unpublished manuscript, vanished into oblivion.

Thirty years after his death, Ifton Rhyn colliery was deepened in conjunction with Brynkinalt colliery at Chirk. It developed into easily the biggest mine in Shropshire and did not close till 1968 – further proof, if more is needed, of his judgement as a mining engineer and practical geologist.[9] But Davies' everlasting memorial is his writings, in style lucid and warm, even at times intimate, – prose of a kind rarely encountered in similar works today.

Of his sermons he recorded 'I have striven to put first principles and great truths in clear simple language to ordinary men and women'. And true to form the prefaces to his best known volume express no lofty ambition, but rather a desire 'to illustrate great principles' and 'simply to set forth, for ordinary English readers, the substance of our knowledge on metalliferous minerals and mining'.

This is Davies the orphan and Davies the lay preacher, to whom God, geology and mining all formed part of a great and indivisible unity. His books were sermons and his readers, the congregation.

Sources and Acknowledgements to First Edition

The bibliography of copper mining in Snowdonia is very meagre. The subject attracted scant attention from contemporary writers, except in passing, and even the Geological Survey's Special Reports are but a shadow of their Mid-Wales counter-part. The main source has therefore been archival evidence assisted in the 19th century by *The Mining Journal* - an invaluable if not unimpartial record. Several recent articles and papers are also very informative, but limited resources has prevented more than a cursory glance into the treasure-chest of local newspapers.

The origins of the various sources are explained by numbering the text, without it is hoped, reducing the narrative to a bibliographical clothes-line in the process, and obscurities like *ibid* and *op. cit.* have been avoided.

In compiling this account the help of others has been indispensable. Particularly I have to thank George Hall for making available his *Mining Journal* references, for compiling the 1848-1913 production table, and for his companionship and guidance in early visits to the region. Jeremy Wilkinson has kindly extracted a great deal of information from the Public Record Office and other sources, and I am also indebted to Gareth Davies for various material, particularly relating to the Porthmadog-Beddgelert area.

Alasdair Neill has rendered much assistance with references, field notes and interpretation, and I have to thank John Burman and Ifor Higgon for photographs and sketches, and not least for their company on a number of visits to sites during the past few years.

In addition, for their help in a variety of ways I am indebted to Russell Bayles, Justin Brooke, Peter Challis, Amina Chatwin, Peter Crew, Mr. & Mrs. A. Evans, W.R. Evason, J.B. Groucott, the late A.K. Hamilton Jenkin, Elfed and Evan Roberts, Dr. M.J.T. Lewis, Douglas McLean, Dr. George Ryback, Cedric Titcombe, Dr. Hugh Torrens, Dr. T.E. Vaughan, R.W. Vernon, John Wellington, C.J. Williams, and Lloyd Williams.

I am also grateful to the staffs of the National Library of Wales, Gwynedd Archive Services, the University College of Wales Library, Shropshire County Record Office, The Institution of Mining and Metallurgy Library, and the British Museum. Lastly, I have again to thank my wife for typing a manuscript which, with the inevitable amendments and additions, at times seemed interminable.

Acknowledgments to Third Edition

A number of friends and acquaintances have contributed, in particular Susan Ashmole, Adrian Barrell, George Hall, Harold Morris and C.J. Williams. Margaret Dunn has drawn my attention to material relating to Beddgelert and Nant Gwynant, and for a variety of help I must also thank John Bennett, Peter Crew, Roy Fellows, Alasdair Neill, Jon Knowles, Steffan ab Owain, Lindsey Porter, Emyr Searell, Simon Timberlake, and Alison and Tim Wilkinson. I am indebted to them all. The plan on page 117 was drawn by Keith Jackson and Olly Burrows.

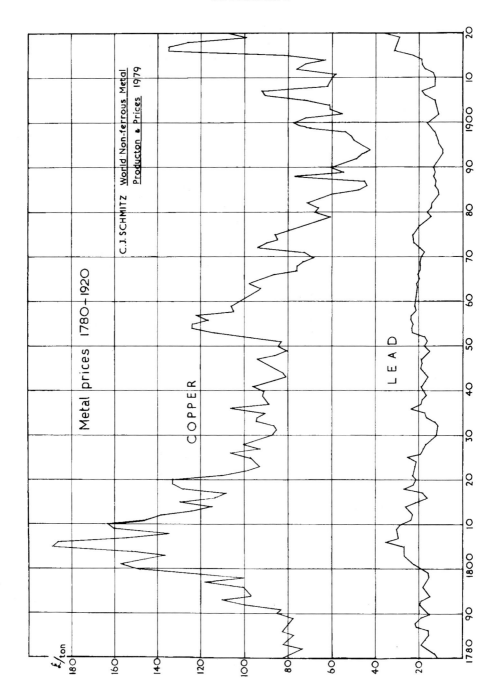

SNOWDONIA COPPER ORE PRODUCTION (1848-1913)
(excluding Llandudno) From Official Statistics

	Tons Ore	Produce %
1850		
Llanberis	110	–
1854		
Snowdon	93	8.2
Gilfach	25	9.0
1855		
D.C.	7+	
S.D.	10+	
Lliwedd	2+	
1857-9		
D.C.	766	10
1860		
D.C.	434	9.4
S.D.	181	10
Snowdon etc	350	7.3
1861		
D.C.	111	9.0
S.D.	3	10
Snowdon	356	7.0
1862		
S.D.	586	6.5
Snowdon	184	6.9
1863		
D.C.	543	7.7
S.D.	428	7.7
Snowdon	130	7.7
1864		
D.C.	575*	
S.D.	401*	
1865		
D.C.	492*	
S.D.	201*	
1867		
D.C.	622	7.9
S.D.	228	5.7
Gwernor	32	6.0
Bangor	29	5.1
Lliwedd	6	5.2
Clogwyn	14	4.8

	Tons Ore	Produce %
1868		
S.D.	83	6.5
Sygun	28	6.4
Hafodyporth	20	6.5
Brynfelin	16	6.5
1869		
Hafodyporth	18	6.4
Lliwedd Bach	3	6.7
Sygun	48	6.8
D.C.	212	9.4
Snowdon	12	4.2
Llanberis	18	14.4
1870		
S.D.	17	8.6
Sygun	2	10
Llanberis	75	34
	187	
S.D.	50	9.0
1872		
D.C.	200	6.5
S.D.	52	6.4
Llanberis	75	5.0
1873		
D.C.	100	10
S.D.	199	7.7
1874		
D.C.	80	7.8
S.D.	59	5.8
Snowdon – 'A Quantity'		
1875		
D.C.	60	
S.D.	38	4.6
1876		
D.C.	12	–
S.D.	36	–
1877		
D.C.	150	6.3
1878-80		
D.C.	565	7.2
Derwen Deg	58	10

	Tons Ore	Produce %
1881		
D.C.	140	7.0
Derwen Deg	20	7.0
1882		
D.C.	180	9.2
S.D.	138	11.8
1883-84		
D.C.	386	9.8
S.D.	72	7.0
1885-86		
D.C.	370	9.5
1889		
Moel Hebog	7	4.5
Pantywrach	5	9.0
1896		
D.C.	1668	(poor ore)
1897-98		
D.C.	90	10.5
1899		
D.C.	13	10
Snowdon	607	9.0
1900		
D.C.	5	10
S.D.	40	14
Snowdon	601	9
1901		
S.D.	34	15
Snowdon	248	10
1902		
D.C.	172	9
1903		
Snowdon	77	8.5
Sygun	410	5.0
D.C.	220	2.0
S.D.	218	17
1910-11		
S.D.	466	16
1913		
Snowdon	124	7.7

DC = Drwsycoed
SD = Simdde Dylluan
*   Figures obtained from Dawson Ware papers
+   Copper Metal.

Notes 1 Several minor entries of uncertain location are omitted.
     2 Prior to 1867, small outputs were apparently ignored.
     3 Statistics for individual mines ceased in 1913.

APPENDIX III

COPPER ORE PRODUCTION

Extracted from **Robert Hunt** *Memoirs of the Geological Survey* **Vol II Part II** 1848, *Mineral Statistics* 1848-1913 and Phillips & Darlington *Records of Mining & Metallurgy* 1857

Sales at Swansea (see below for 1804-1820) compiled by Hunt, and sales from later *Mineral Statistics* (1848-1913)

Mine	1821	22	23	24	25	26	27	28	29	30	31	32	33	34	35	36	37
1 Aberglaslyn																	
2 Bangor*																	
3 Bronsgellog★																	
4 Bronygader			20	18	4												12
5 Brynfelin															29		102
6 Bwlchmwlchan																	
7 Carnarvon*		43															
8 Clogwyn Coch		4							111	32							
9 Cwm*																	23
10 Derwen Deg																	
11 Drwsycoed	75	103	112	53	82	73	27	55	148	417	629	916	561	762	548	333	295
12 Ffestiniog*									8								
13 Gilfach								10	30								
14 Gwernor																	
15 Hafod-y-Llan					23	33											
16 Hafod-y-Porth								20									
17 Llanberis		77	29	91	160	91	205	165	292	469	369	1169	701	859	479	585	770
18 Llandegai*															36	36	43
19 Llandudno, Old	28	84	88	44	169	51	158	118	91	42	94	49	45			53	755
20 Llandudno, New			187	37	71	135	294	501	251	183			132				
21 Lliwedd	53	81	100	65	49	52	35	67	126	63	37			32		52	
22 Lliwedd Bach																	
23 Llwyndu																	
24 Llyndy*								9									
25 Melin Cythan*																	
26 Moel Hebog																	
27 North Wales*																	12
28 Pantywrach						20	6	8	6								
29 Penyralt (Catherine & Jane Consols)																	
30 Simdde Dylluan						17		217	154	412	259	1032	347	301	227	152	134
31 Snowdon ☆	35	20		14					24	22							
32 Sygun				92	129	62		71	75	47							52
33 Ty Gwyn															65		
34 Tyn-y-Wern*																	
Total Tonnage	191	412	536	308	664	581	801	1239	1318	1693	1388	3166	1786	1954	1384	1211	2198

Output 1804-1820 as follows;

Bwlchmwlchan 1806. 12 tons. Carnarvon 1815, 1817, 190 tons.
Drwsycoed 1804, 40 tons; 1813, 28 tons. Llanberis 1816,60 tons.
Llandudno 1808, 1810, 1813-1820, 3605 tons.
Snowdon 1804, 12 tons; 1806-1811, 186 tons, 1819-1820, 83 tons.

38	39	40	41	42	43	44	45	46	47	1804–1847	1848–1913	Total 1804–1913	Swansea sales 1819–56, from Phillips & Darlington. Period	Tons	
26	30									56		56			1
											29	29			2
	8									8		8			3
29		9								92		92	1823–24	38	4
11										142	16	158			5
										12		12			6
							38			271		271	1822	43	7
24	6									177	14	191	1829–30	123½	8
55										78		78			9
											78	78			10
373	434	123					104			6291	6648	12939	1821–40	5960½	11
										8		8			12
										40	25	65			13
											32	32			14
		10		34				81		181		181	1825–26	56	15
										20	38	58	1822–50	7353	16
288	215	147								7221	278	7499			17
53	14									182		182	1838	66½	18
800	697	633	292	184	883	489	625	630	235	10942	1358†	26506	1819–48	9670½	19
315										2106					20
93	160	228	133	303	173					1902	36	1938	1821–43	1730½	21
											3	3			22
		171	294	220						726		726			23
										9		9			24
			370							370		370			25
											7	7			26
										12		12	1855	67½	27
										40	5	45			28
07	52									159		159	1838–39	134½	29
305	317	136								4010	3709	7719	1827–40	3884½	30
				32						428	2732	3160	1820–29	151½	31
94	62		91	34						909	488	1397	1825–38	629½	32
09										174		174	1836–39	174½	33
									11	11		11			34
782	1995	1457	1271	750	1022	530	767	711	246	36577	27696	64273			

MGSSR Vol XXX, 51

Inconsistent with Hunt's figures.

Mineral Statistics 1860 for 'Cwmdyle etc.' Is 350 tons. Cwmdyle (Snowdon) has been assumed as 300 tons.

Location not established, in some cases perhaps outside Snowdonia.

Presumably near Bronsygellog farm, workings at 730350, 730345

INDUSTRIAL ARCHAEOLOGY - SUBSTANTIAL REMNANTS

Notes: Prior permission to view should be obtained where sites are on private
property. The new Ordnance maps show rights of way.
Old workings are potentially dangerous and should not be approached too closely.
In addition to details below, nearly every site displays opencuts, shafts, adits and
dressing areas.

Mine	Page	Wheel Pit(s)	Crusher house	Tramway	Incline	Whim Circle
C. & J. Consols	19	*				
Gilfach	32	*	*			
Cwm Ciprwth	32	Waterwheel and winding drum, with flat rods				
Cwmdwyfor	38	*	*		*	*
Dolgeth	36	*	*		* (slate)	
Drwsycoed	44		*			
Simdde Dylluan	53	*				*
Benallt	56			*	*	
Brynfelin	63	Magazine				*
Aberglaslyn	64	*				
Nantmor	68	Aerial Ropeway		Mill Site		
Sygun	70	*	Museum	*	Elmore mill site	
Llwyndu	70	Calcining flue?				*
Braich-yr-oen	85			*	*	
Hafod-y-porth	89	*	*			
Hafod-y-llan	85	*	*	*		
Lliwedd	93	*	*			
Snowdon	98	*	*	*		
Clogwyn Coch	111	*		*	*	
Ceunant	118	Arsenic flues				
Llandudno	124	Course of Brammock-rods		Museum	Bronze Age Mine	

GLOSSARY

ADIT	A tunnel driven for access and drainage.
AGENT	A vague term, generally a manager or promoter.
BLENDE	Zinc ore, zinc sulphide.
CAPTAIN	A mine manager or foreman.
COBBING	Breaking down the crude ore with hammers to remove the waste rock.
COPPER-PYRITES	The common ore of copper, of a brassy colour, containing copper and iron sulphides.
CROSS-CUT	A level or adit driven in order to cut a lode.
CRUSHER	A machine having two revolving cylinders separated by a small gap for crushing ore.
ENGINE SHAFT	A shaft fitted with pumping equipment.
FATHOM	6 feet, the miner's unit of measurement.
FLAT-RODS	Iron rods about 20ft long linked together to transmit power from a waterwheel or rotative engine to the pumping shaft.
GALENA	The common ore of lead, lead sulphide, up to 86% lead.
GOSSAN	The weathered upper part of a lode.
KIBBLE	A barrel-shaped vessel of iron or wood in which ore was raised.
LAUNDERS	Long wooden troughs, usually to convey water onto a waterwheel.
LEVEL	A tunnel or gallery, usually on the course of a lode.
MALACHITE	Copper carbonate. A very rich ore.
MUNDIC	A form of iron pyrites.
ORE-DRESSING	Separating the ore from the waste rock.
QUARTZ	Silicon dioxide. A glassy appearance if pure; more usually milk-white.
RISE	An underground shaft driven upwards.
SETT	An area of land taken for mining purposes.
STOPES	The working chambers or cavities in a mine created by removal of ore.
TRIBUTORS	Miners who receive payment in proportion to the value of ore raised.
WHIM	A large windlass worked by horses, steam or water-power for winding ore.
WINZE	An underground shaft excavated downwards.

NOTES AND REFERENCES

Recurring references are indicated as follows:

AW — Archaeology in Wales
Bick — David Bick, *The Old Metal Mines of Mid-Wales,* parts 1-6, 1974-91
Boyd — J.I.C. Boyd, *Narrow Gauge Railways in South Caernarvonshire,* 1972
C & DH — *Carnarvon & Denbigh Herald*
Crew — P. Crew, 'The Copper Mines of Llanberis & Clogwyn Goch', *Caern. Hist. Soc.* 1976
Evans — J. Evans, *Beauties of England & Wales*
GAS — Gwynedd Archives Service
Hall — G.W. Hall, *The Gold Mines of Merioneth,* 1975
IMR — Inspector of Mines Reports.
MGSSR — Memoirs of the Geological Survey, *Special Reports on the Mineral Resources of Great Britain*
MJ — *The Mining Journal*
Morrison — T.A. Morrison, *Goldmining in Western Merioneth,* 1975.
MW — *The Mining World*
Neill — John & Ruth Neill, 'The Copper Mines of Snowdonia', *Climber's Club Journal* XIV No.2, 1962.
NLW — National Library of Wales, Aberystwyth
PRO — Public Record Office, Kew.
Rees — D. Morgan Rees, 'Copper Mining in North Wales' *Arch. Camb.,* 1968
UCNW — University College of North Wales Library, Bangor.
Vaynol — Vaynol Estate papers, Gwynedd Archives Service.

Introduction (pages 7-11)

1 The secretary is Dr David Roe, 20 Lutterburn St, Ugborough, Devon, PL21 0NG
2 Subsequent to stoping, the freshly exposed surface of copper-pyrites or galena remaining in the lode commences to oxidize, and the thickness of deposit could form a rough guide to the age of the workings. For an introduction to ancient mining, see R. Shepherd, *Prehistoric Mining and Allied Industries,* 1980.
3 John Percy, *Metallurgy* 1861, 302. This source is recommended for the history and practice of copper smelting, calcining and allied operations.
4 The Cornish returns regularly exceeded this figure *every year!*
5 Clwyd R.O., d/KK/133
6 Robert Hunt, 'Mines, Minerals & Miners', *The Mining & Smelting Magazine* 1863, Vol III, 35.
7 As a boy, Auden wanted to become a miner, and his book 'Machinery for Metalliferous Mines' by E.H. Davies, was still in his library when he died.
8 David Bick, 'The Welsh Mines Preservation Trust', Managing the Industrial Heritage, Leicester University Archaeology Monographs No2, 1995. The secretary of the trust is Graham Levins, email:graham.levins@virgin.net
9 Evidence before the Kinniard Commission, 1863, (question 19,278) described metal miners of 25 or 26 as 'middle-aged'.

The Earliest Mines in Snowdonia (pp 12-15)

1 See also Crew & Crew (eds), 'Early Mining in the British Isles', 1990 Plas Tan y Bwlch. Ford and Willies, 'Mining Before Powder' 1994 PDHMS
2 Oliver Davies, *Roman Mines in Europe,* 1935
3 Timberlake 5, AW 38, 1998, 79-81. Bruck, J (ed) Timberlake, S 'Mining and Prospection in Early Bronze Age Britain' 2001. Bronze Age Landscapes, Oxbow Books 179-192. See also David Bick, *The Old Metal Mines of Mid-Wales,* Part 6, 1991, 53-61
4 Paul T Craddock, *Early Metal Mining and Production* 1995, 11, 58
5 Mighall et al, 'Bronze Age Lead Mining at Copa Hill- Fact or Fantasy?' 2000, Journal of the Historical Metallurgy Society Vol 34 Part 1. See also Timberlake, S et al. 'Excavations on Copa Hill, Cwmystwyth' 2003. British Archaeological Monograph, Oxford
6 Ref 4, 144
7 Sue Jones, AW 39, 1999, 79
8 Sir James Frazer, *The Golden Bough* Various editions.
9 David Bick, 'Bronze Age Copper Mining in Wales - Fact or Fantasy?' 1999, JHMS, Vol 33 Part 1
10 R C Turner & R G Scaife, 'Bog Bodies' 1995, British Museum Press.
11 Boshier AK, 'Mining Genesis' 1969, Mining Survey No. 64, 21-8 Johannesburg. This paper sheds valuable light on ancient mining

and smelting, with the beliefs and rituals involved. These had an important bearing on the physical processes and archaeological testimony left behind.

12 John Percy, *Metallurgy* 1861, 289

Porthmadog (pages 16-27)

1   **NLW** Price of Rhiwlas papers, 161.
2   Memoirs of Samuel Holland *Merioneth Hist. Soc.* 1952, 11.
3   **NLW** Price of Rhiwlas papers, 165.
4   **Hall**, 58. *MGSSR* Vol XXX, 42. Morrison, 23.
5   **NLW** Harrison Deeds. Box 65, parcel 2
6   *Y Gestiana* 1892, Alltud Eifion
7   **MJ** 1845, 550.
8   For further references to this mine, see **Boyd** 17, 19, 22, 35.
9   Reference 6 mentions lead works restarted here in the 1820s. There was a lead mine at Llidiart-y-Spitty in 1755. See **NLW**, Price of Rhiwlas papers, 73.
10 David Morris. *Portmadoc and its Resources,* 1856.
11 **MGSSR**, Vol XXX, 40.
12 For drawings of a similar enginehouse, see **Barton**, *The Cornish Beam Engine,* 197. Only two enginehouses now remain at mines in north-west Wales - Penrhynddu near Abersoch and Mona, near Amlwch. See D.E.Bick 'The Beam Enginehouse in Wales' Industrial Archaeology Review 1989, 84-93. A 68 inch engine survives complete, at Dorothea slate quarry, Nantlle.
13 MacEwen, *National Park, Conservation & Cosmetics* 1980. Allen & Unwin.
14 Bob Owen, *Diwydiannau Coll*
15 The subsequent account is largely based on **MJ**.
16 J.R. Foster-Smith *The Mines of Merioneth,* Northern Mines Research Society. The lead ore figure seems optimistic.
17 **GAS** X/D8/4/943,944
18 **PRO** BT31/1820/7043
19 **PRO** BT3I/2575/11748
20 **GAS** X/D8/4/946
21 For the technology of waterwheels applied to mining, see **Bick** Part 1, 40-47.
22 Parc and Croesor papers, NLW. I am indebted to Adrian Barrell for drawing my attention to this site.
23 Bob Owen 'Diwydiannau Coll'.

Cwm Pennant (pages 28-43)

1   **PRO** CREST 15/85, 7.15/86,225
2   **MJ**. 1853, 98, 176. I am grateful to Dr. M.J.T. Lewis for pointing out the site.
3   **MJ**. 1853, 298, 397
4   **MJ**. 1853, 760
5   **MJ**. 1853, 816
6   **MJ**. 1854, 14
7   For more of Berdan and his machine, see **Hall**, 23-25.
8   **PRO**. CREST 15/88, 95

9   **PRO**. BT 31/3705/2304
10 **IMR**
11 **PRO** BT 31/4418/28746
12 **Rees**, 183
13 **MJ**. 1850, 348
14 **MJ**. 1889, 207
15a **IMR**
15b **GAS** Vaynol XM/6914/17/6
16 For further details, see Russell Bayles, Northern Mines Research Society Memoirs Vol.2 No.1
17a Francis Dingey & Son appears in Kelly's Directory for 1873 and 1883, but not 1893.
17b **GAS** Vaynol XD/35/20
17c The Britten Pan was a large iron pestle and mortar usually worked by waterpower for extracting gold by pulverising the ore with mercury to form an amalgam. It was widely used in the Dolgellau goldbelt for nearly a hundred years. There is a restored example in the Forestry Visitor Centre at Maesgwm, north of Dolgellau. For more details, see G W Hall, *The Gold Mines of Merioneth* 1975
17d Alun John Richards *A Gazeteer of the Welsh Slate Industry*, 1991, 97
17e According to *Cwm Pennant*, written about 1890 by Gwilym Roberts, the house was built by a mining or quarrying company.
18 **MJ**. 1868, 770, 773
19 **MW**. 1872, 984
20 For full details of the Gorseddau tramway, see **Boyd**.
21 **MJ**. January-July 1876, passim. *The Mining Journal* is recommended as a valuable source for transport historians.
22 **MW** 1876, 462
23 Davies was North Wales correspondent to *The Mining Journal*.
24 **MW**. 1876, 535
25 **MW** 1876, 834
26 **MW**. 1876, 856
27 For the subsequent fate of the company see Bick. Part 3,41
28 **MJ**. 1879, 1123

Nantlle Vale (pages 44-62)

1   W.J. Lewis. *Lead Mining in Wales.* 1967, 104.
2   **NLW**. Powis 3047
3   **NLW**. Powis 3380
4   **GAS**. Vaynol 2516
5   **Rees**, 176
6   J. Eardley-Wilmot. *Reminiscences of the late Thomas Assheton Smith* c. 1859
7   **Crew**, 73
8   **Vaynol** 5665-6872
9   Vaynol papers
10 Vaynol 5057
11 PRO BT 31/2215/10443
12 A level, apparently of some antiquity, on a powerful quartz vein at 555528 was perhaps driven for gold.

13 Home Office, *Mineral Statistics*.
14 **MGSSR**. Vol XXX, 49
15 **GAS** Xm/Maps/298.
16 **GAS**, M/416
17 Information from the late Will Richards, Dylife.
18 Deduced from the 1st and 2nd edn 6 inch Ordnance maps.
19 **Vaynol** 2516. MJ 1870, 526. Clwyd R.O. D/KK/329,333
20 **MGSSR** Vol XXX, 48, 49
21 Minutes of Evidence, *Condition of All Mines in Great Britain* 1864. (Kinniard Commission) North Wales, 329 et seq.
22 **MJ** 1876, 617. John Roberts, *Miners Assoc. Devon & Cornwall* 1873/4, 41-43
23 **MJ** 1876, 591. Much of the following derives from **MJ**
24 **PRO** BT3 1/2598/13680. In the 1840s Dawkes was architect to the Birmingham & Gloucester Railway, and of various neo-gothic buildings in Cheltenham. See Bryan Little, *Cheltenham in Pictures*, 1967.
25 Prospectus, **PRO** BT3 1/32708/208396
26 See **Bick**, Part 4, 41-45
27 **MJ** 1845, 89
28 **MJ** 1870, 9, 104. Much of the following derives from **MJ**
29 Probably John Kitto, manager of Brynpostig mine, See **Bick**, Part 4, 48-50.
30 Probably David Forbes, F.R.S.
31 Kitto had also worked at Laxey, and may have recommended Casement. The latter's name is perpetuated on the 72ft diameter pumping wheel at Laxey built in 1854, where a plaque reads *Richard Rowe manager; Robert Casement engineer*. Glanville turned up later at Talybont mine in Cardiganshire, another dubious promotion. See **Bick**, part 3, 38.
32 Phillips & Darlington, *Records of Mining & Metallurgy* 1857, 197
33 **MJ**. 1871, 1041
34 **MJ** 1873, 157
35 Clwyd R.O. D/DM/448/72
36 Dawson Ware papers in possession of G.W. Hall.
37 **Bick** Part 4, 9-11.
38 Clwyd R.O. D/KK/333, **C & DH**. 27 July 1844., See also GAS. X/M/1778/7
39 **NLW** Druid Inn papers.
40 **GAS** BJC. 277

Beddgelert (pages 63-84)
1a Gruffyd Pritchard, 'Mynfeydd Eryic'. *Cymru*, June 1901
1b David Jenkins 'Beddgelert; its Facts, Fairies and Folklore', 1899, 6
1c J R Harris 'The Copper King', 2003, 18 **New Edition by Landmark Publishing**
2 For details see **Bick** Part 3, 6-8. Also David E. Bick, 'Remnants of Mining in Ceredigion before the 19th Century', *Ceredigion* 1978, 355-359
3 S. Dawson Ware, quoting Bob Owen papers
4 William Williams, *Observations on the Snowdon Mountains*, 1802
5 *North Wales Gazette* 5 Jan 1808
6 **MJ** 1851, 585
7 **PRO** BT 31/550/2230
8 **MJ** 1861, 184, 213, 229, 286, 449
9 **C & DH** 23 July 1875
10 **GAS** Dorothea 2045
11 **NLW** Powis 3078, 3607, 2953. Details of the mine in 1786 are given in a letter to W.W.Wynn, Clwyd Record Office, Ruthin, DD/WY5350 See also Grant-Francis, *The Smelting of Copper in the Swansea District* 1881, 117-120
12 **Evans**, 158
13 I am indebted to Alsadair Neill for this information.
14 Bob Owen *Diwydiannau Coll.*
15a **Boyd** 276
15b For more details, see David Bick *A History of Sygun* 1987
16 Sygun ores went to Amlwch between 1820 & 1830; See **UCNW**. Mona mine letters 2746, Mona smelting works account.
17 The next few pages are based on **NLW** G.E. Owen Collection Box 54, which contains the full story of Llwyndu, the mine's history otherwise being virtually unknown.
18 Dunkin also invested in Cardiganshire lead mines. See **Bick** Part 2, 17.
19 Ironically, Llechfraith later worked successfully in conjunction with Clogau as a gold mine, and it has since re-opened. See **Hall** 32,64. In 1836 Byers was lessee of East Cwmheisian, (742282) where gold was discovered in 1843; See **Morrison**. 29, 98.
20 Information from Dr. M.J.T. Lewis
21 *North Wales Chronicle* 24 Sept 1839
22 **C & DH** 3 April 1841. UCNW Mostyn 7059, 7060
23 **UCNW**. Searell papers.
24 Probably John Petherick, agent to Mona and Llanberis mines in 1866. A man of this name was consulting engineer to the Consolidated Copper Mines of Cobre; see W.J. Henwood *Trans R.G.S. Cornwall* Vol VIII, 591
25 **IMR**
26 **MJ** 1883, 909
27 **MJ** 21 May 1904
28 A. Stanley Elmore, 'The Invention of the Flotation Process'. *Mining & Scientific Press* 23 Sept. 1916
29a F.E. Elmore; Patent No 21, 948. It appears by defining claims too narrowly he left the door open for competitors. See *The Illustrated Official Journal (Patents)* 24 Feb 1969, 124-148
29b See Peter R Jenkins *The Glasdir Experiment* 1991

30 *Skinner's Mining Manual, Directory of Directors.*
31 **MJ** 20 Dec 1902
32 Walter McDermott. 'The Concentration of Ores by Oil'. *Mineral Industry* 1902, 697-707; details of plants at Clogau St. Davids and Tywarnhaile are also included. Hugh Pugh diaries, **GAS** Dolgellau.
33 **MJ** 22 Feb., 8 Mar., 12 April 1902
34 **Morrison,** 47
35 **Neill** 73

Nant Gwynant (pages 85-97)
1   Howel Williams, 'Geology of Snowdon' *QJGS* Vol 83,378
2   **UCNW** Mostyn 7034, 7047, 7049
3   The following principally derives from the Searell papers **UCNW**
4   **MJ** 1847, 161
5   For further details of the quarry, see Jean Lindsay, *A History of the North Wales Slate Industry* 1974, 13,152
6   D.C. Davies, *Slate & Slate Quarrying* 1878,46
7   **IMR**
8   Clwyd RO/DKK/333. The mine is referred to as Hafod Boeth.
9   **C & DH** 22 March 1845
10 **MJ** 1864, 153
11 **UCNW** Baron Hill 6466
12 The mine is described in G.W. Hall, *Metal Mines of Southern Wales* 1971
13a The Old Series Ordnance maps marked mineral lodes, and also, by means of alchemical symbols, the metals they contained. The hand-coloured one inch geological maps with the lodes embellished in gold paint were based upon them; they are a delight, and now collectors' items.
13b This period is based on A Ivor Pryce Deeds & Dues, and Church in Wales Records, NLW
14 **MJ** 1853, 502
15 **UCNW** Searell papers M57. Rees 191 equates Lliwedd with Lliwedd Bach and Hafod-y- llan, but quotes no authority.
16 Dawson Ware papers in possession of G.W. Hall
17 Howel Williams, 'Geology of Snowdon' *QJGS* Vol 83, 408

Snowdon (pages 98-116)
1a Perhaps Snowdon was re-discovered like the Parys copper mine in Anglesey, earlier worked by the Romans. Prehistoric copper smelting refuse has been found in the neighbourhood. See Oliver Davies, *Roman Mines in Europe* 1935, 176
1b For details of the mineralogy, geology and underground workings, see Colman and Laffoley, 'Brittania or Snowdon Mine', PDHMS Bulletin, 1986, 313-31
1c GAS Vaynol X/Poole/5835,5838

2   Anon, *A Tour in Wales & through several Counties of England* 1806, 100
3   **Neill** 74
4a **UCNW** MS 908 (Hyde-Hall MSS)
4b Marion Addis & Pam Inder *The 1844 Diary of John William Sneyd* 1996
4c John A Robey & Lindsey Porter *The Copper and Lead Mines of Ecton Hill, Staffordshire* 1972, 68-75
5   **MJ** 1847, 328
6   **MJ** 1850, 265, 268, 353
7   Much of the mine's history 1851-75 is derived from **M.J**
8   **PRO** BT41/180/1027
9   **PRO** BT3I/290/1003, letter on file.
10 **Rees,** 197
11 **UCNW** Baron Hill MS 6473
12 D. C. Davies *Metaliferous Minerals and Mining*, 4th Edn 1888, 399
13 Home Office, List of Mines.
14 **Neill,** 75
15 Information received from R.W. Vernon
16 **PRO** BT3I/15949/56779
17 Climbers' Club Journal, Feb. 1899. The 6 inch Ordnance map 1919 edition, revised 1912, shows the ropeway's course.
18 Unpublished notes of the late Arthur Lockwood, of the Cwm Dyli hydro-electric power station. I am indebted to Alasdair Neill for this material.
19 See **Neill** for further details of the paths & industrial archaeology.
20 **Evans,** 424
21 **Crew,** 74
22 **GAS** Vaynol 5358, 5053
23 **MJ** 1873,323
24a **Neill,** 72
24b David Bick 'Llanberis Copper Mine', AW 1988,85
25 **GAS** Vaynol 2515
26 **Crew,** 64
27 A. Aitkin, *Journal of a Tour through North Wales,* 1797, 119-120
28 **Evans,** 422. The author apparently 'lifted' part of his description from Aitkin.
29 The aqueduct can be seen in H.L. Jones, *Illustrations of the Natural Scenery of the Snowdon Mountains,* 1829. The picture is reproduced in Crew's paper.
30 R. Fenton, **UCNW** MS 908 (Hyde-Hall MSS), 181,194
31 **Vaynol** 517
32 **Crew,** 73
33 **MJ** 1873, 526. Cragg was later a promoter of the Snowdon Mountain Railway.
34 **PRO** BT 31/1858/7315
35 Phillips & Darlington, *Records of Mining & Metallurgy* 1857, 198-199. See also *The Mining and Smelting Magazine* Vol III, 101

Nant Ffrancon (pages 117-120)

1   **MGSSR** Vol XXX, 50
2   W. Williams, *Observations on the Snowdon Mountains,* 1802, 120
3   T.M. Bassett, 'Diwydiart yr Nyffryn Ogwen'. *Caern Hist. Soc*
4   **MGSSR** Vol XV, 44
5   **UCNW** Bangor, 9754
6   **UCNW** Penrhyn, 2212
7   D.C. Davies, *Earthy Minerals & Mining,* 3rd Edn 1892, 308
8   **UCNW** Bangor 2037
9   **MJ** 1847, 328
10 **MJ** 1852, 28, 31
11 **MJ** 1852, 324
12 A three-roll mill was erected in 1854 at a mine near Penmaenpool, Dolgellau; see **Hall** 34. For a brief history and description of crushing rolls, see **Bick**, Part 2, 46-49.
13 Old Series Ordnance; **UCNW** Penrhyn, 2037, 2212
14 W. Williams, *Observations* 1802, 122-3.
15 H.D. Hughes, *Antiquities of Llandegai and Llanllechid* 1866, 132
16 **UCNW** 908 (Hyde-Hall mas), 92

Conwy and Llandudno (pages 121-131)

1a S. Lewis, *Topographical Dictionary of Wales*
1b For more details of the mine, see John Bennett & R.W.Vernon,1997, *Mines of the Gwydyr Forest*, Part 7, 74-86
2   **MJ** 1877, 742. Much of the following account derives from this source. See also various files in **PRO**
3   North Wales Freehold Copper Mines. Mining Record Office, Health & Safety Executive.
4   For the features in 1888, see 1st edn 25 inch Ordnance map.
5   Sir Arthur Russell, *Mineralogical Magazine* 1944, 5-7
6   J. & C. Walker, 'Geological Map of England & Wales & Part of Scotland'. 1837. Another Bwlch at 807789 actually agrees more closely with the map. The only other source of antimony which I have encountered in Wales is the rare silver-copper-antimony sulphide *Polytelite,* which David Forbes identified at Tyddyn Gwladys (736267), a mine extensively stoped above deep adit. See *Phil Mag* March 1868.
7   C.J. Williams, *The Llandudno Copper Mines,* Northern Mine Research Soc. 1979.
8   G.D.B. Jones, *Subterranean Britain,* 85-86. John Baker, 1979.
9   The origin of the term "brammock-rods' is obscure.
10 W. Vivian. 'Native copper in Llandudno Mine', Q.J.G.S. 15, 109-110.
11 D.C. Davies, *Metalliferous Minerals & Mining,* 4th edition, 138. For an illustrated account of the orebodies, see Robert Hunt, *British Mining,* 456, 2nd edn, 1887.
12 Clwyd R.O. DIKK/8/4.
13 **C.& DH** 5 March 1842.
14 Other big Sims engines worked at Carn Brea, Ting-Tang Consols, Perran Great St. George and Foxdale, Isle of Msn.

Ffestiniog (pages 132-136)

1   'Mines of the Gwydyr Forest', Part 5, 102
2   B.D.T. Lynas 'The Migneint Area', J. Geol. Soc. London 1973, 497
3   **MJ** 1850, 265; 1854, 247
4a **MJ** 1878, 825
4b Samuel Lewis 'Topographical Dictionary' 1834
5   **MGSSR** Vol XXIII, 54-55
6a Clwyd R.O. D/DM1448/81
6b Y Gwladgarwr 1839,32
7   **MGSSR** Vol XXX, 41

D.C. Davies, F.G.S. (pages 137-144)

1   The substance of this chapter derives from some 80 letters written by Davies to William Whitwell, which I aquired many years ago, and are now deposited in **NLW**. Other sources include the *Dictionary of National Biography* and similar works.
2   Information from commercial directories.
3   A bookseller's catalogue has come to hand listing G.C. Davies *Wildcat Tower; or; the Adventures of four boys in pursuit of Sport and Natural History in the North Countrie,* Frederick Warne & Co., 1st edition 1877. G.C. Davies' 'Handbook to the Rivers and Broads of Norfolk and Suffolk' had gone to 44 editions by 1913.
4   For further details see **Bick** part 5, 42, 43
5   D.C. Davies, Q.J.G.S. Vol 33, 10-28 D.S.I.R. *The Geology of the Country Around Wrexham* Pt II, 128
6   For further details see **Bick** Part 3, 43
7   D.A. Bassett, *Biography and Index of Geology for Wales* 1963, lists 30 publications between 1858 and 1885, but is incomplete in this subject alone. A full list has yet to be compiled.
8   Henry Davies gained wide experience abroad, and something of his career may be gleaned from his *Machinery for Metalliferous Mines,* first published in 1894.
9   For a photograph and details, see I.J. Brown, *The Mines of Shropshire,* 82.

Dr T.E. Vaughan tells me that in 1965 he visited the grave of D.C. Davies, wife and daughter. The stone was about 50 yards west of the chapel in Oswestry Cemetry, and his inscription read: 'In loving memory of David Christopher Davies who died at sea, Sept 19th 1885 aged 58 years, 'Be ye also ready for in such an hour as ye think not, the Son of Man cometh.'

INDEX

Note: Mines denoted by capital letters